Canadian Curriculum Press
Forward Learning

COMPLETE CANADIAN
READING

K

- Developmental Skills Checklist • Basic Skills
- Reading Readiness • Early Reading Skills
- Parent Suggestions

Conforms to Ministry of Education Guidelines

A Note to Parents:

Your child will enjoy these colourful learning activities designed to reinforce the curriculum taught in Canadian schools. You can help your child make the most of each learning session by:

- reading the directions aloud and moving your finger under each word while your child watches;
- doing one or two questions together to ensure your child understands what to do, then letting him or her work independently;
- praising your child's efforts and working at a pace that is comfortable for him or her; and
- maintaining your child's enthusiasm by making each session short, pleasant, and part of your routine.

Activities marked "Challenge" are designed to stretch children's thinking beyond expectations. If your child doesn't seem ready for them, just skip them for now and come back to them later. Most children will need a little more parental support to work through the Challenge activities. Since all children develop at their own pace, it is important to let your child's interest guide you in providing just the right amount of challenge.

Completing the activities in this Complete Canadian workbook will help your child build a solid foundation of skills—and confidence—for success at school and beyond!

Sincerely,
Elaine J. Kenny, B.Ed.

For special bulk purchases, please contact: sales@canadiancurriculumpress.ca.

For other inquiries, please contact: inquiries@canadiancurriculumpress.ca.

ISBN 978-1-77062-907-3
Canadian co-author: Elaine J. Kenny, B.Ed.
Senior Series Editor: Lisa Penttilä
Layout: Michael P. Brodey
Cover Design: Laura Brunton
Selected illustrations: Andrea Scobie

With the participation of the Government of Canada | Canadä

Printed in Canada

Table of Contents

Early Reading Skills

What to Expect From Your Child by the End of Kindergarten

Language

Your child . . .

- uses language effectively to express his or her needs and wants to interact with others.
- can speak in complete sentences.
- asks many questions and looks for answers.
- enjoys being read to and talked to by adults.
- enjoys sharing information about him or herself and his or her family.
- enjoys language play, nonsense rhymes, songs, riddles, and jokes.
- practises using words and language heard in school.

Cognitive Development

Your child . . .

- has a much longer attention span and can listen to longer, more involved stories.
- can follow multiple-step directions.
- concentrates on tasks from beginning to end.
- is beginning to identify left and right.
- can name basic colours and shapes.
- can copy basic designs and shapes.
- can understand concepts of number, size, position, and time (such as days of the week).
- associates the number of objects with the written numeral.
- can recognize letters and identify the sounds they make.
- is able to print his or her own name.
- can read familiar words.

Motor Development

Your child . . .

- can control his or her large muscles. He or she can hop on one foot; jump over objects; and throw, bounce, and catch a ball easily. Your child can also run, climb, skip, tumble, and dance to music.
- is able to dress and clean him or herself.
- is developing greater control over his or her small muscles. He or she should now be able to tie his or her own shoelaces and manage buttons and zippers.
- can cut on lines and use a paintbrush, crayons, markers, clay, and glue.
- can print uppercase and lowercase letters and his or her name.

Social/Emotional Development

Your child . . ..

- is social and enjoys interacting with other children.
- is curious and has an active imagination.
- is confident but still needs praise and encouragement when trying new things.

Developmental Skills Checklist

This checklist is designed to help you record and assess your child's progress in the following kindergarten skills. Write the date next to each skill as your child masters it, writing any other comments you may have about your child's progress. You may also want to add to or adapt this checklist to fit your child's abilities.

Basic Skills

• Names basic colours _____

• Names simple shapes _____

• Identifies opposites _____

• Understands positional concepts _____

• Names days of the week in order _____

Reading Readiness

• Follows multiple-step verbal directions _____

• Recites the alphabet _____

• Identifies uppercase letters in random order _____

• Identifies lowercase letters in random order _____

• Matches uppercase and lowercase letters _____

• Identifies sounds made by letters _____

• Identifies characters in stories _____

• Identifies setting in stories _____

• Can retell a story _____

• Identifies problem/solution in a story _____

• Reads colour words _____

• Reads some words by sight _____

Developmental Skills Checklist

Mathematics Readiness

- Counts objects to 20 _____
- Writes numbers to 20 _____
- Identifies numbers to 20 in random order _____
- Rote counts to 100 _____
- Counts by 10's to 100 _____
- Uses ordinal numbers _____
- Reads a simple graph _____
- Identifies and continues established patterns with one attribute_____

Writing Readiness

- Dictates a sentence about a picture _____
- Prints from left to right_____
- Leaves spaces between words _____
- Prints some words independently_____
- Prints own sentences using sounds_____
- Uses basic punctuation in sentences (eg. capital, period) _____

Fine (Small) Motor Skills

- Colours within lines _____
- Draws shapes _____
- Holds a pencil _____
- Prints letters and numbers_____
- Cuts a line with scissors _____

Suggestions for Parents

The following pages offer suggestions for games and activities that parents can use to help their children build skills and understand concepts that they will encounter in school. Most of these activities require little preparation or materials. Have fun while you play and challenge your child!

Basic Skills

- Write your child's name on a sheet of paper. Then, have your child trace over it with different coloured markers to make a rainbow effect.

- Create "name art" with your child. Have your child write his or her name on a sheet of paper and illustrate it.

- Help your child learn his or her full name, address, and telephone number. Explain situations when it is important for your child to be able to provide this information.

- Sing and dance the "Hokey Pokey" with your child to practise the concepts of left and right.

- Discuss types of weather. Ask your child to identify the clothes that he or she would wear when the weather is rainy, snowy, hot, etc.

- Look at family pictures with your child. Discuss some of the things that are the same about family members as well as some of the things that make them unique individuals.

- Talk with your child about foods he or she likes to eat. Talk about why certain foods are good for people and where they come from. Help your child understand where foods come from before they go to the grocery store. Group foods by food group: fruits, vegetables, sweets, grains, etc.

Suggestions for Parents

- Find pictures of animals and have your child name them. Help your child learn the names for the animal babies and the sounds the animals make.

- Talk about the importance of trees to our environment (homes for animals, food, shade, clean air). You may want to read the book *Backyard Birds* by Robert Bateman and Ian Coutts.

- Plant seeds with your child and keep a record of what happens. Talk about the order in which the changes occur.

- Make a chart with your child that lists his or her daily routine. For example: 8 o'clock—time to get up. Talk about the sequence in which he or she does things.

- Have a "Things That Go Together" scavenger hunt. Make a list of things found around the house that need "partners" (or use the objects themselves) and have your child search the house for them. For example: A toothbrush needs _____. Peanut butter needs _____.

- Play a colour search game. Ask your child to find as many things as he or she can that are the colour you name.

- Buy fingerpaints and allow your child to experiment, mixing them to make other colours.

- Bake a cake or make cutout cookies with your child and allow him or her to mix food colouring into white frosting to create different colours of frosting.

- Set out an assortment of dried beans. Have your child sort them into piles by shape, size, and colour.

Suggestions for Parents

- Take a walk with your child and encourage him or her to pick up "treasures" along the way. After returning home, ask your child how he or she could sort the treasures into groups and have him or her do so.

- Have your child put away the silverware. Have him or her sort the forks, knives, small spoons, and large spoons.

- Have your child organize his or her clothes by type or colour.

- Talk with your child about ways his or her toys and books could be organized by how they are alike in colour, size, etc.

- Play "Mommy or Daddy Says" the same way "Simon Says" is played. Give your child verbal directions. He or she is to follow them only if preceded by the words "Mommy Says" or "Daddy Says."

- Give your child directions in three or four steps. Say them clearly and in order, holding up a finger as you say each one. See how well your child can remember your directions and follow them.

Squares	Circles

- Look for shapes around the house. Make a list of things that are circles, squares, rectangles, and triangles.

- Help your child observe shapes in nature. Take a walk and collect leaves, seeds, nuts, stones, etc. Have your child sort them into groups by shape, then by colour and size.

Suggestions for Parents

- Find opportunities around the house to compare things that are big and small. Have your child compare objects, focusing on their size.

- Have your child trace your hand. Then, have your child trace his or her own hand and compare the sizes. Whose hand is bigger? Whose is smaller? Who has longer fingers? Whose fingers are shorter?

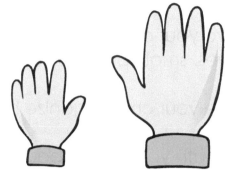

- Have your child use paper clips to measure things around the house. Challenge him or her to think of other units that could be used to measure (spoons, pencils, etc.).

- Take out different-sized glasses and cups. Let your child experiment filling and emptying them. Talk to your child about the concepts of full and empty.

- While experimenting with the cups, help your child count the number of times you must pour liquid from a small cup to fill a larger one. Talk about the relationship between sizes.

- Have your child make a bead necklace using a pattern that he or she develops. Check to be sure there is consistency throughout the pattern.

- Lay similar objects on the table in a pattern and have your child identify the pattern.

Suggestions for Parents

- Set objects on, below, and between each other on the kitchen table. Ask your child where the objects are located. Have your child move the objects and quiz you!

Reading

- Read to and with your child every day to foster a lifelong love of books and reading. Let your child sit on your lap or beside you so that he or she can see the pictures as you read. Point to the words you read, and if there are repeated refrains in the books you read, pause at those points and let your child supply the words.

- Be sure your child sees you reading. Let him or her know how important reading is in your life, both at home and on the job.

- Call attention to the pictures in the books you read and talk about them with your child.

- Stop as you are reading a story and ask your child what he or she thinks will happen next.

- Talk to your child about the characters in the stories and the setting.

- Talk about the sequence of the story. Have your child tell you what happened first, in the middle, and at the end.

Suggestions for Parents

- Help your child understand that print has meaning by encouraging him or her to "read" cereal boxes and other print around the house.

- Look for print on street and business signs and have your child "read" it. Explain what these signs mean and why they are important.

- Encourage your child to point out letters he or she recognizes in print and practise spelling words he or she sees frequently. Use magazines, newspapers, and colouring books to help your child create letter and word collages.

- Label objects around the house so that your child will learn to associate the objects with the printed words. Index cards written with coloured markers work well.

- Focus on a "letter of the day" (or week) in your home. Help your child look for that letter in print and think of words that begin with that letter.

- Create a chart labeled with colour words. Go through magazines with your child and let him or her find pictures that are that colour, gluing them on the correct section of the chart.

- Go through the grocery ads and have your child cut out the pictures and words. Play a matching game.

Suggestions for Parents

- Buy magnetic letters and put them on the refrigerator. Encourage your child to spell words with them.

- Create your own ABC book or list of words your child can write. Let your child illustrate the book.

- Play "I Spy" with your child. ("I spy something that begins with the letter **A**.") Have your child guess what it is.

- Play "I'm Thinking of a Letter." Give your child different clues about a letter. See how many clues it takes for him or her to guess it. Then, have your child think of a letter for you to guess.

- Have your child shape cooked spaghetti into each of the letters of the alphabet. He or she could then make objects that begin with each letter.

- Give your child old magazines. Give him or her directions such as "Circle all the **m**'s." Continue with various directions, making sure to include different letters of the alphabet.

- Make sugar cookie dough and have your child form letters and words with the dough. Then, bake the letters and let your child eat his or her favourite words. Don't forget to have him or her say the sound the letter makes as he or she eats it.

Suggestions for Parents

- Go through photo albums and let your child select a picture from each year of his or her life. Help your child sequence them. He or she may want to write his or her age or a brief caption underneath each picture.

- Encourage relatives or friends to send postcards or special occasion cards to your child to encourage him or her to read.

- Make frequent trips to the library and let your child explore the books there, choosing some favourites to take home for you to read.

- Ask grandparents, other family members, or friends to recommend books that they liked as a child and have them tell your child why they liked them.

- Arrange a book swap with families of other young children so the children can read their friends' favourite books.

- Have your child dictate a story using greeting card or magazine pictures. Write the story for your child and help him or her read it.

Writing

- Provide your child with many different writing materials—pens, pencils, markers, crayons, paints—and many kinds of paper—writing paper, greeting cards, postcards, invitations, etc. Encourage your child to write and to draw illustrations.

Suggestions for Parents

- Keep your child's writing materials in a special place where they can be used independently.

- Buy a notebook for your child's writing. Let him or her decorate it and make it special. Encourage your child to write in the notebook every day. When your child writes something, provide opportunities for him or her to share it with you.

- When your child draws a picture, have him or her write a caption or dictate a caption for you to write. Be sure to write exactly what your child dictates.

- Encourage your child to help you when you are writing: making grocery lists, writing notes and letters, etc. Talk about how writing is important to you.

- Provide chalk and a chalkboard for your child.

- Spend time writing outdoors with your child. Write with sidewalk chalk all over the driveway.

- Take a trip to the beach with your child and use sticks to write words in the sand. Read what you write to each other.

- Enter art or colouring or writing contests often. This encourages creativity, finished work, and the possibility of publishing your child's work.

- Use your computer as a writing tool. Have your child type the alphabet or short messages on the screen. Print out the finished products.

Suggestions for Parents

- Make pudding with your child. Spread it on a cookie sheet and let your child write words he or she knows with his or her fingers!

- When on a trip, help your child write postcards home to family and friends.

- Write a book about your child and your family. Use pictures of family members or events. Have your child dictate captions to you or let him or her write them him- or herself. Punch holes in the pages and fasten them together.

Math

- Encourage your child to find numbers around the house (clocks, television, telephone, etc.) and tell you how they are used.

- Look for and read numbers as you ride in the car: street signs, house numbers, at gas stations and other businesses, licence plate numbers, etc.

- Tell your child how you use numbers in your job and at home.

- Look for numbers in the grocery store. Have your child help you find the prices of items.

- Label different household items with "prices" and play store with your child.

Suggestions for Parents

- Capitalize on everyday opportunities to count with your child and to have him or her practise counting. Count cans in the cupboard as you put them away, count books on the bookshelf, or toys as they are picked up.

- Have your child listen and identify the number of times that you make a special noise like clapping or snapping your fingers.

- Let your child play counting and number games with blocks. For example, count how many blocks tall you can make a tower before it topples!

- Make number cards from index cards. Write a number from **1** to **20** on each card and have your child practise putting them in order.

- Give your child a number card and a supply of small objects (macaroni, beads, blocks, etc.) and have him or her practise counting the correct number of objects. Let your child practise with many different numbers. Then, count out a number of objects and have your child match the correct number card to it.

- Say a number and have your child tell you what number comes after it or before it.

- Use magazine pictures to make a counting book. Write a number on each page and have your child cut out pictures of that number of objects on the page.

Suggestions for Parents

- Find numbers in catalogues and let your child practise reading them.

- Punch ten holes in an old greeting card cover with a nice picture. Number the holes. Give your child a piece of string and have him or her thread the holes in the correct order.

- Sing "This Old Man" with your child, having him or her use fingers to represent the numbers.

- Look for books and songs that incorporate numbers, such as *Loonies and Toonies: A Canadian Number Book* by Mike Ilmer and Melanie Rose.

- Use the calendar to help your child with number recognition. Talk with your child about the date and month and count the number of days until a special event.

- Place different numbers of objects in an egg carton to give your child practice counting numbers to **12**.

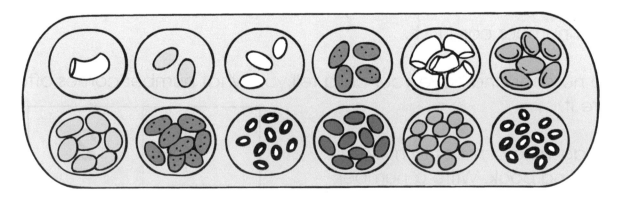

- Number clothespins from **1** to **12**. Label index cards with the number words on one side and the corresponding number of dots on the other side. Play a game with your child, having him or her clip the clothespins on the correct card.

Suggestions for Parents

- Challenge your child to count back from **10**.

- Have your child practise counting by tens. Hold up all ten fingers each time he or she says a number.

- Have your child shape clay into each of the numbers from **1** to **20**.

- Draw a number on your child's back with your finger. Have your child tell you what number you drew. Then, let your child draw a number on your back.

- Read *Canada Counts* by Charles Pachter with your child.

- Talk with your child about ways he or she helps at home. Ask: How can learning to count help us in setting the table?

- Put out a small pile of coins and have your child practise sorting and naming them. Have pennies, nickels, dimes, and quarters available for your child to manipulate. Have your child count how many there are of each coin and talk about the value of each coin. Although pennies are no longer in circulation they are useful as counters.

- Have your child help set the table. Help him or her use one napkin for each plate, one fork for each napkin, etc.

Suggestions for Parents

• Using a bag of marshmallows, have your child give you some marshmallows and take some for him or herself. Talk about who has more and who has fewer. Then, divide the marshmallows equally.

Red

Directions: Colour 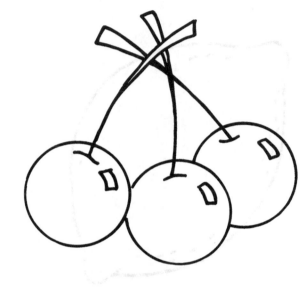 each picture **red**. Then, **draw** a picture of something else red.

Name _____

Yellow

Directions: Colour  each picture yellow. Then, **draw** a picture of something else yellow.

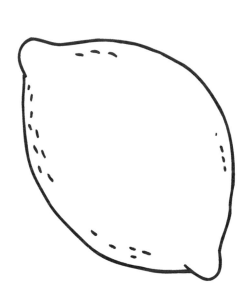

Blue

Directions: Circle  the **blue** picture in each row.

Green

Directions: Colour  each picture **green**. Then, **draw** a picture of something else green.

Orange

Directions: Circle  the **orange** picture in each row.

Purple

Directions: Colour  each picture **purple**. Then, **draw** a picture of something else purple.

GRAPE JELLY

Black

Directions: Circle  the black picture in each row.

Brown

Directions: Circle  the **brown** picture in each row.

Circles

Circles can be different sizes.

Directions: Trace  the circles below. Then, **colour** the

pictures.

31

Squares

Squares have 4 sides of the same length.

Directions: Help Bina get home. **Colour**  the path that has only squares. ☐

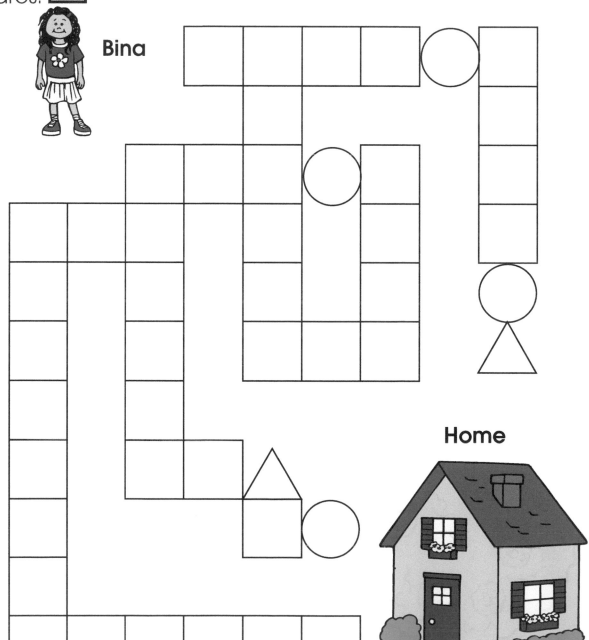

Bina

Home

Triangles

All triangles have 3 sides. Triangles can be different sizes.

Directions: Trace 🖍 and **colour** 🖍 the triangle shapes below.

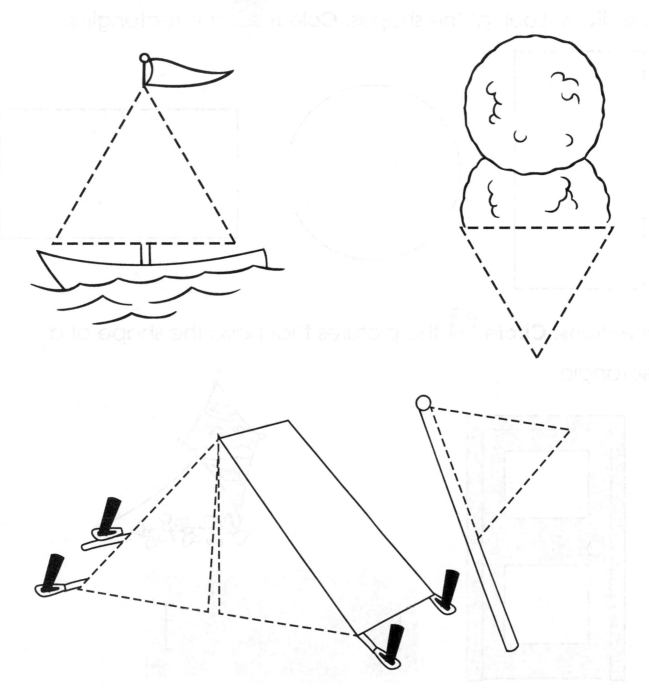

Rectangles

All rectangles have 4 sides, but only the opposite sides are the same length. ☐

Directions: Look at the shapes. **Colour** 🖍 the rectangles.

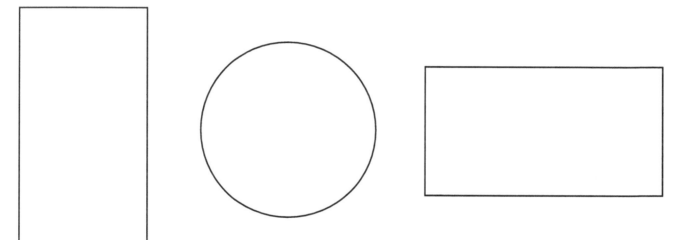

Directions: Circle ✏ the pictures that have the shape of a rectangle.

Get in Shape

Directions: Colour  the ☐ s yellow. **Colour** the ◯ s blue.
Colour the ▲ s red. **Colour** the ▬ s green.

Ovals

Ovals can be different sizes.

Directions: Colour 🖍 the oval shapes below.

Rhombuses

Rhombuses can be different sizes.

Directions: Trace each rhombus in the designs below.

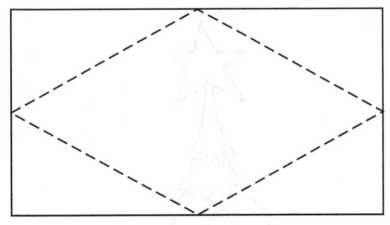

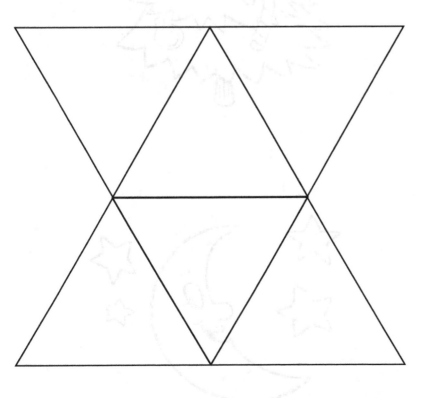

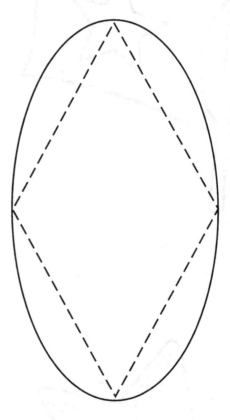

How many
did you find?_____

Stars

Stars can be different sizes.

Directions: Colour the star shapes below.

Hearts

Hearts can be different sizes.

Directions: Colour the heart shapes below.

Big

Look at the pictures in each box.

Directions: Circle  the pictures that are big.

Small

Look at the pictures in each box.

Directions: Circle  the pictures that are small.

Long

Look at the pictures in each box.

Directions: Circle 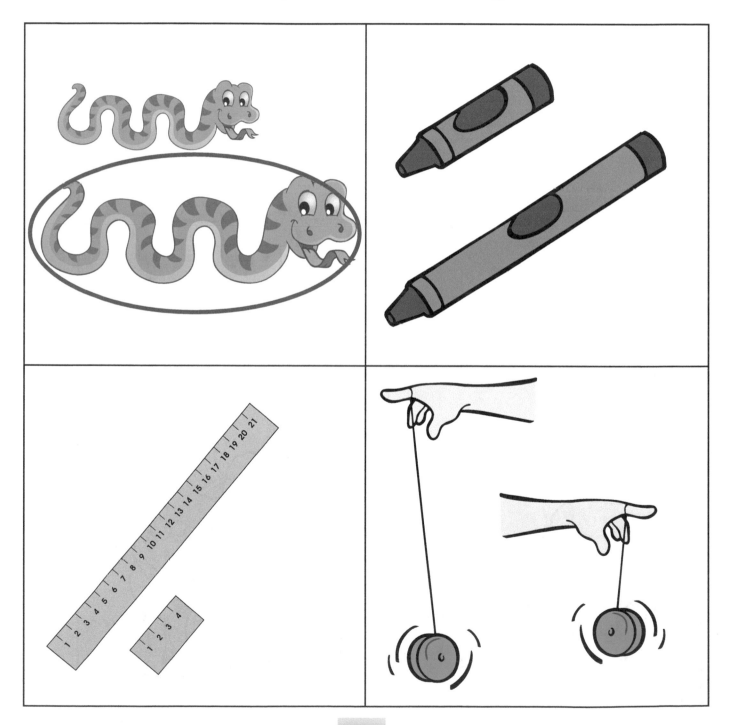 the pictures that are long.

42

Short

Look at the pictures in each box.

Directions: Circle  the pictures that are short.

Hey Shorty!

These worms were told to line up in order from shortest to longest. But something is wrong. The worm that should be first is not where it belongs!

Directions: Circle  the worm that is out of order.

Tall

Look at the pictures in each box.

Directions: Circle  the pictures that are tall.

Short

Look at the pictures in each box.

Directions: Circle  the pictures that are short.

Jack, Jill, and John Higgins

Jack, Jill, and John Higgins are all cousins. Jack is very small. Jill is very tall. And John is right in the middle.

Directions: In the space between Jack and Jill, **draw**  a picture of John Higgins.

Name _____

Mike's Moose in Alberta

Mike lives in Alberta. A family of moose lives in Mike's backyard! Each moose is a little bit taller than the next moose.

Directions: Circle  the tallest moose with a **red** crayon. **Circle** the shortest moose with a **blue** crayon. Draw an **X** on the middle moose.

How many tips are on the tallest moose's antlers? _____

How tall do you want to be? _____

Growing Up

Directions: Colour 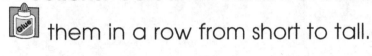 and **cut out** the people below. **Glue** them in a row from short to tall.

Fast and Slow at Lake Diefenbaker, Saskatchewan

Look at the picture of Lake Diefenbaker below.

Directions: Circle  the things that go fast.

Draw an **X** on each thing that goes slowly.

Name _____

Opposites on Thanksgiving Day!

Doug just helped his mom set all of the food on the table for Thanksgiving Day. Which things on the table are hot?

Directions: Circle  all of the hot things with a **red** crayon.

Which things on the table are cold? Circle all of the cold

things with a **blue** crayon.

What kinds of food do you eat on Thanksgiving Day?

Opposites at the Hockey Game

Belinda just went to her first hockey game. Many people sat in the bleachers watching it.

Directions:

Which person is sitting on something soft?

Colour  that person **pink**.

Which person is sitting on something hard?
Colour that person **purple**.

Which person is very happy? **Colour** that person **yellow**.

Which person is very sad? **Colour** that person **blue**.

Which person is very short? **Colour** that person **red**.

Which person is tall? **Colour** that person **orange**.

Opposites!

Directions: Look at the pictures below. **Draw**  a line to match each picture to its opposite.

More Opposites

Directions: Look at the pictures below. **Draw** a line to match each picture to its opposite.

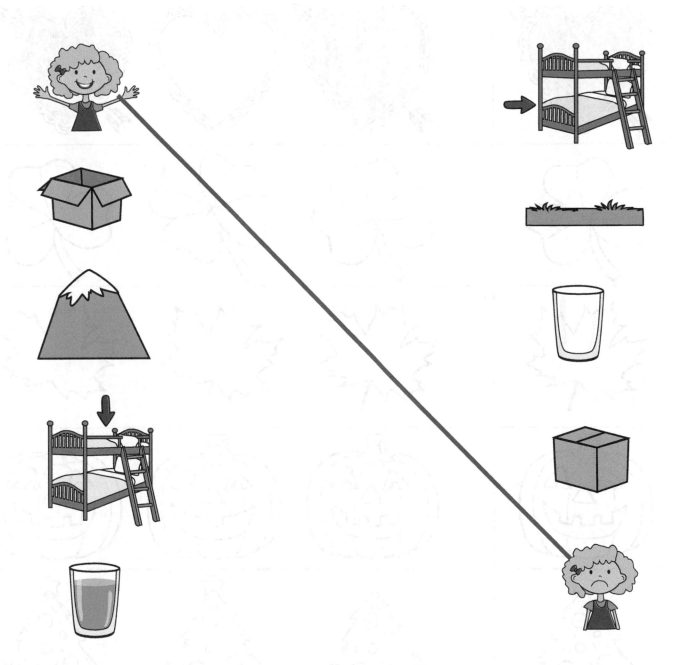

55

Picture Match

Directions: Colour 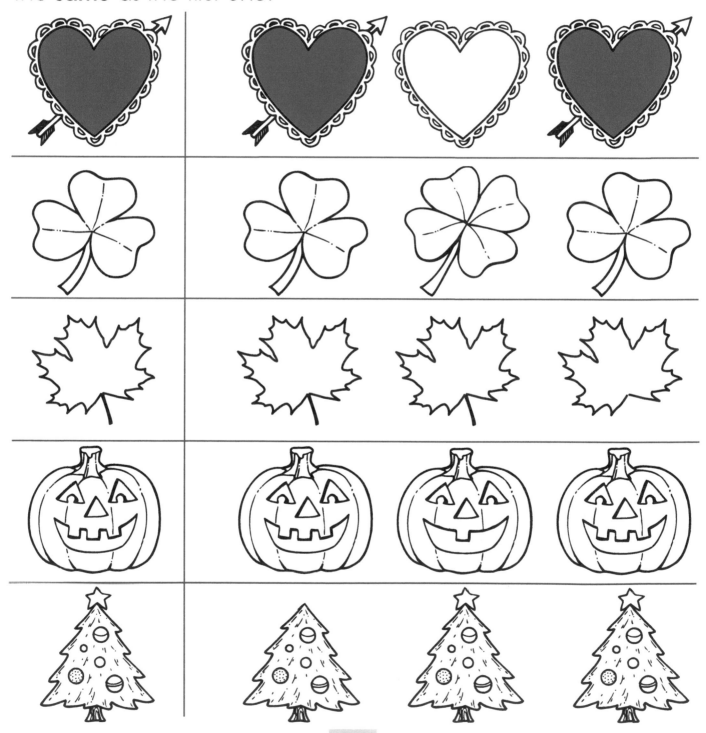 the first picture. Colour each picture that is the **same** as the first one.

Ship Shape

Directions: Draw 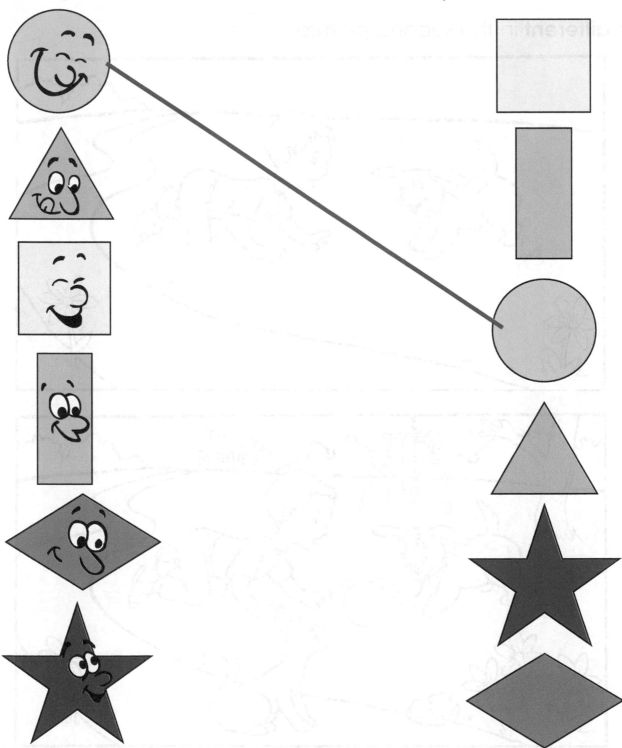 a line to match each shape.

Same and Different

Directions: Colour  the first picture. **Circle** the things that are **different** in the second picture.

58

A Complete Picture

Directions: Draw  the missing parts to make the pictures look the same. **Colour** the pictures with the same colours.

Dinosaur Match

Directions: Draw  a line to match each dinosaur with its skeleton.

Farm Animal Patterns

Make a memory game.

Directions: Cut out 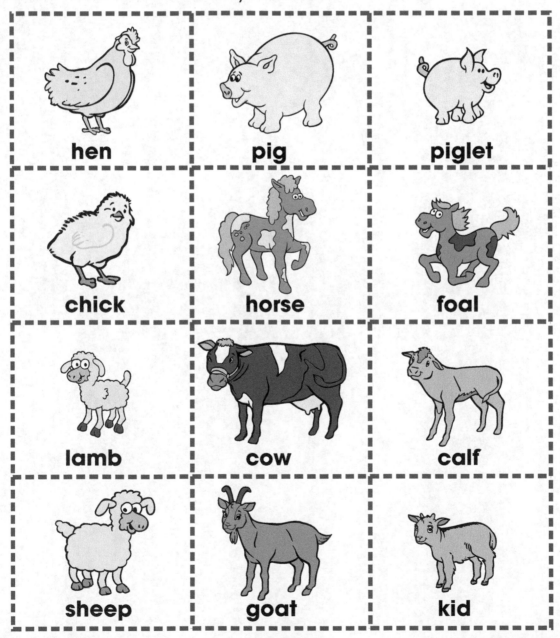 the cards and place them face down.

Play the game with a partner. Take turns turning the cards over

to match mother and baby animals.

hen

pig

piglet

chick

horse

foal

lamb

cow

calf

sheep

goat

kid

Shadow Shapes

Directions: Look at the shadow shapes in the first row.

Draw 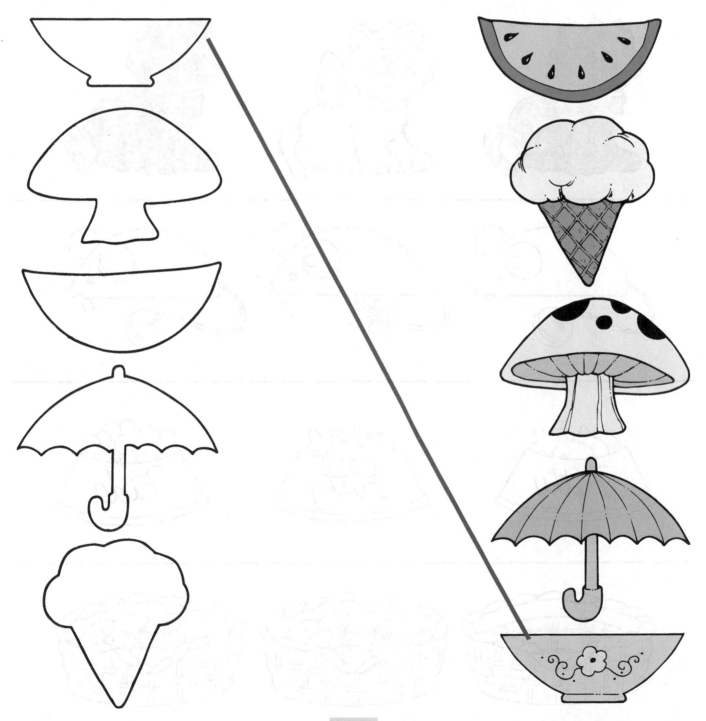 a line from each shadow to the picture it matches.

Name _____

Same and Different

Directions: Colour  the two pictures in each row that are the **same**.

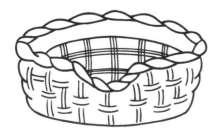  

Samantha's Hats

Samantha loves hats. Look at all the hats on her shelves. One hat on each shelf is different from the others.

Directions: Colour the hat that is **different**.

The Tortoise and the Hare

Look at the tortoise and the hare below. Can you name two ways that they are the same?

Can you name two ways that they are different?

What would you name the tortoise?

What would you name the hare?

Directions: If the tortoise and the hare were in a race, who do you think would win? **Circle** 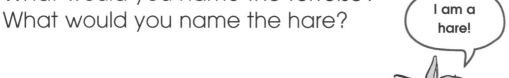 your choice.

Basketball!

Coby loves to play basketball. In fact, he has 6 pairs of sneakers just for basketball!

Directions: Draw a line to connect each pair of matching shoes.

Circle your favourite pair of shoes above.

Fred the Peacock

Look at Fred the Peacock. ➡️

Directions: Only 1 of the peacocks below is exactly like Fred. **Circle**  it. What is different about each of the other peacocks?

Fred

68

Lollipop, Lollipops

There are lots of lollipops in the candy store.

Directions: In each row below, **circle** the lollipop that is the same as the one in the jar at the beginning of the row.

69

Butterfly, Butterflies

A butterfly is a type of insect. It has 4 wings. Only 2 of the butterflies below look the same.

Directions: Can you find the 2 matching butterflies? **Draw** a line to connect them.

Pair of Dragonflies

Look at all the dragonflies. Only 2 dragonflies are exactly the same. Can you find them?

Directions: Circle 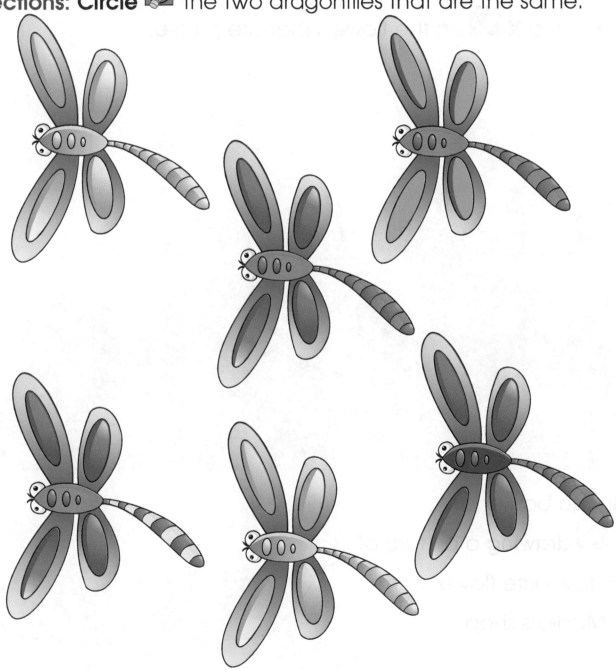 the two dragonflies that are the same.

Ms. Marilla's Flowers

Ms. Marilla owns a flower shop. She sells only flowers that are purple or pink.

Directions: Circle  the flowers that are **pink**.

Draw a big **X** on the flowers that are **purple**.

Fill in the basket by **drawing** a picture of your favourite flower from Ms. Marilla's shop.

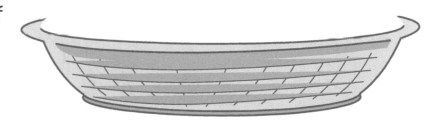

You Choose

Look at the animals below.

Which animals have feathers?
Which animals have no legs?
Which animals would be fun to ride?

Directions: Circle the animal that would make the best pet for you.

Canada's Forest Creatures

Many animals live in the forest. Find the animals that are small.
Which animals are large? Which animal do you think is scaly?
Which animals are soft?

Which animal would you want for a pet? Why?

Directions: Circle your favourite animal above.

Pat and Fred

Pat the puffin and Fred the fox got lost at the amusement park. Help them find their families.

Pat **Fred**

Directions: Use a **black** crayon to **draw**  a line connecting everyone in Pat's family together. Use an **orange** crayon to **draw** a line connecting everyone in Fred's family together.

So Soft

Which objects below are soft?

Directions: Colour  all of the soft things **red**. **Colour** the rest of the objects in a way that makes sense.

Part of a Group

Directions: Pick 3 pictures that go together in each group. Draw an **X**  on the picture that does **not** belong in the group.

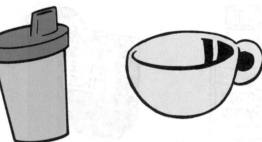

 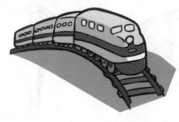  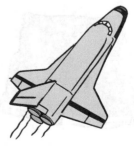

Three Things

Directions: Circle  your answers below.

Which 3 things are on your hand?

Which 3 things would you need if you were sick?

    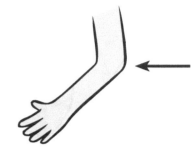

Which 3 things are in the sky?

Which 3 things would you wear if you were hot?

Cold Creatures

Many different kinds of animals live in the cold. Some of the animals pictured below live in cold places and some do not. Which animals do not belong?

Directions: Draw an **X**  on the animals that do **not** belong in a cold place.

79

Name _____

The Ice-Cream Truck

Alexander and Jonathan hear the bells on the ice-cream truck. They want to buy ice-cream cones. The ice-cream truck stops, and they study the ice-cream menu. But something is very strange. There are things on the menu that do not belong.

Directions: Draw an **X** on the 3 things that do **not** belong on the menu.

Wrong Purple Things

There are lots of purple things in the picture below. Some of them are not supposed to be purple!

Directions: Draw an X  on the 5 things that should **not** be **purple**.

What Does Not Belong?

In each row below, use the clue to find the answer.

Directions: Draw an **X**  on the picture that does **not** begin with the letter **A**.

Draw an **X** on the picture that does **not** begin with the letter **J**.

Draw an **X** on the picture that does **not** begin with the letter **S**.

Draw an **X** on the picture that does **not** begin with the letter **T**.

Kooky Kangaroos

Choose one of the kangaroos, and explain why it does **not** belong with the others. Then, choose another kangaroo and find a new reason why it does **not** belong with the other kangaroos.

Directions: Circle  the kangaroo you like best and explain why.

What Goes Together?

Directions: Draw a line to match each thing that goes together.

What Belongs?

Directions: Draw an **X**  on each thing that does **not** belong in the grocery store.

Stranger Safety

Directions: Draw an  on the pictures that are not safe.

Colour the pictures that are safe.

Name _____

Above

Look at the picture. The sun is above the bird.

Directions: Circle  the pictures **above** the bird.

Name _____

Below

Look at the picture. The car is below the bird.

Directions: Put an  on pictures **below** the bird.

Between

Directions: Trace and **colour** the cat that is **between** the other cats.

Colour the mouse that is **between** the other mice.

Between

Directions: Trace  **and colour** the shapes that are **between** the others.

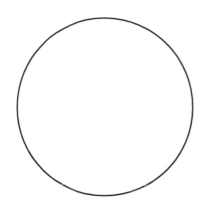 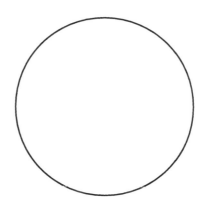 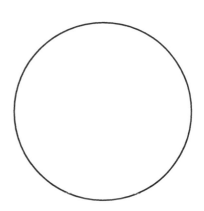

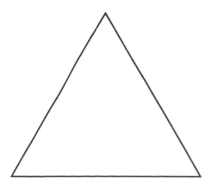 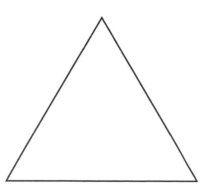 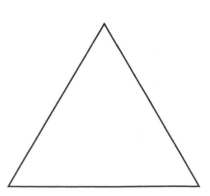

Where Does It Go?

Directions: Colour and **cut out** the pictures at the bottom of the page. **Glue** them in the correct place.

| under | on |
| between | in |

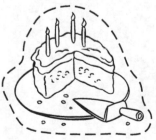

First, Middle, Last

Directions: Look at each group of three things. **Colour**  the **first** thing **green**. **Colour** the **middle** thing **purple**. **Colour** the **last** thing **orange**.

Left and Right

Directions: Colour the picture on the **left blue. Colour** the

picture on the **right red**.

Example:

left   right

Left and Right

Directions: Colour 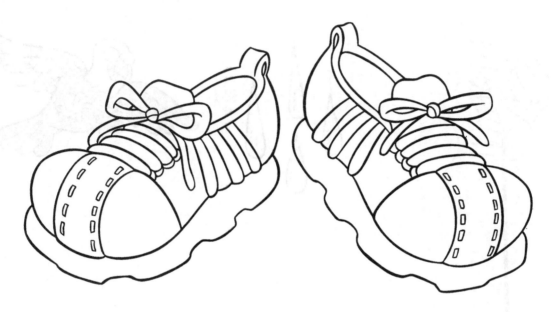 the pictures on the **left** green. **Colour** the pictures on the **right** orange.

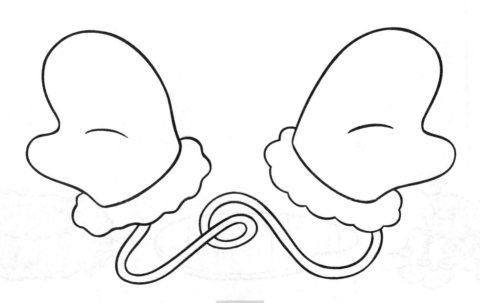

Top to Bottom

Directions: Draw  a line from the **top** picture to the **bottom** picture.

Name _____

Top to Bottom

Directions: Draw  a line from the **top** picture to the **bottom** picture.

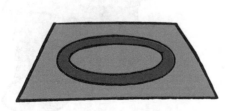

Left to Right

Directions: Draw  a line from the picture on the **left** to the picture on the **right**.

Left to Right

Directions: Draw  a line from the picture on the **left** to the

picture on the **right**.

Home You Go!

Help the animals get home.

Directions: Draw  a line from each animal to its home.

Letter Aa

Directions: Trace and **print** 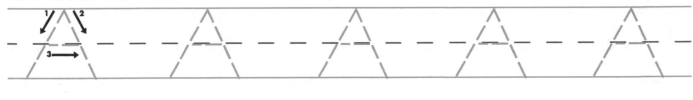 the letters.

UPPERCASE

lowercase

Directions: The pictures begin with the letter **Aa**.

Colour  the pictures.

Letter Bb

Directions: Trace and **print**  the letters.

UPPERCASE

lowercase

Directions: The pictures begin with the letter **Bb**.

Colour the pictures.

Letter Cc

Directions: Trace and **print**  the letters.

UPPERCASE

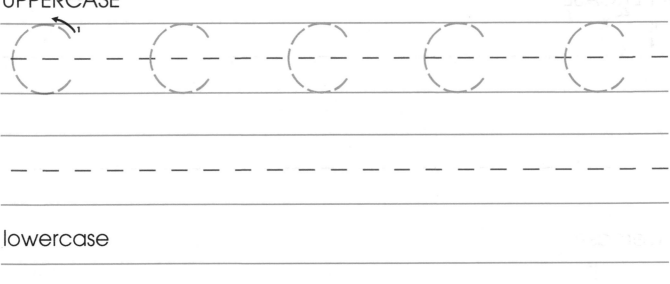

lowercase

Directions: The pictures begin with the letter **Cc**.

Colour  the pictures.

Letter Dd

Directions: Trace and **print** 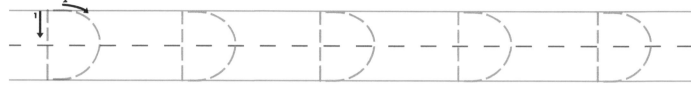 the letters.

UPPERCASE

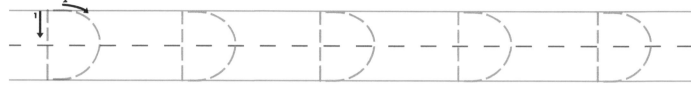

lowercase

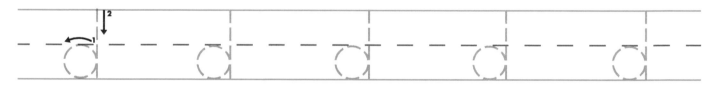

Directions: The pictures begin with the letter **Dd**.

Colour  the pictures.

Letter Ee

Directions: Trace and **print**  the letters.

UPPERCASE

lowercase

Directions: The pictures begin with the letter **Ee**.

Colour the pictures.

Letter Ff

Directions: Trace and **print** 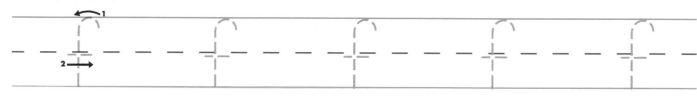 the letters.

UPPERCASE

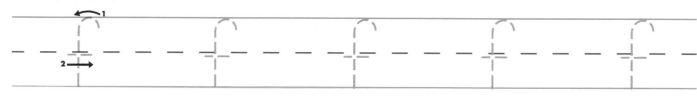

lowercase

Directions: The pictures begin with the letter **Ff**.

Colour  the pictures.

Letter Gg

Directions: Trace and **print** 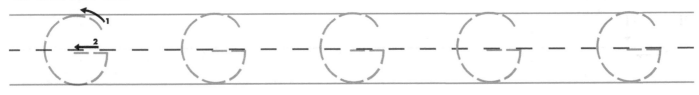 the letters.

UPPERCASE

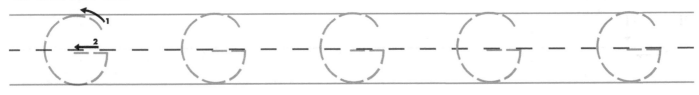

lowercase

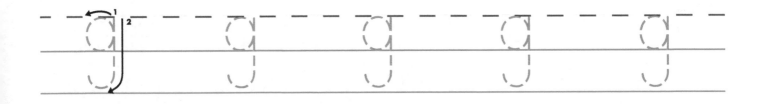

Directions: The pictures begin with the letter **Gg**.

Colour  the pictures.

Name _____

Letter Hh

Directions: Trace and **print** 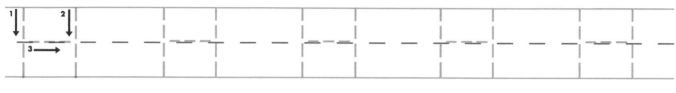 the letters.

UPPERCASE

lowercase

Directions: The pictures begin with the letter **Hh**.

Colour the pictures.

Letter Ii

Directions: Trace and **print**  the letters.

UPPERCASE

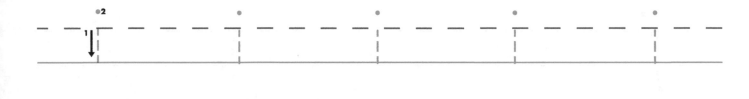

lowercase

Directions: The pictures begin with the letter **Ii**.

Colour the pictures.

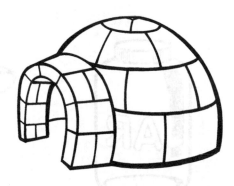

Letter Jj

Directions: Trace and **print** 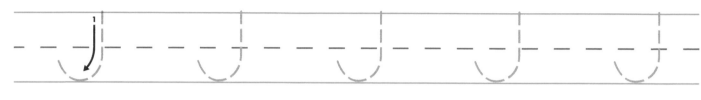 the letters.

UPPERCASE

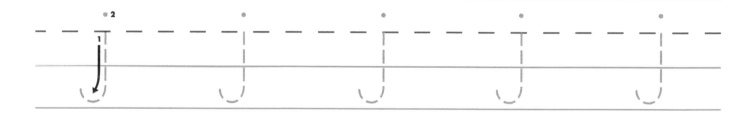

lowercase

Directions: The pictures begin with the letter **Jj**.

Colour  the pictures.

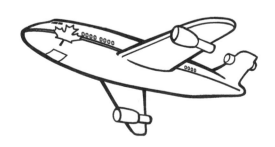 

Letter Kk

Directions: Trace and **print**  the letters.

UPPERCASE

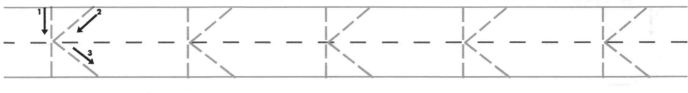

lowercase

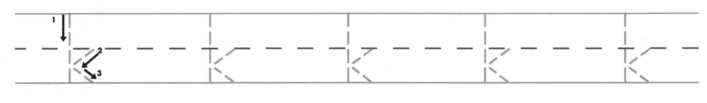

Directions: The pictures begin with the letter **Kk**.

Colour  the pictures.

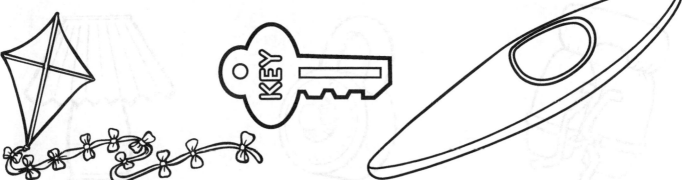

Letter Ll

Directions: Trace and **print**  the letters.

UPPERCASE

lowercase

Directions: The pictures begin with the letter **Ll**.

Colour the pictures.

Letter Mm

Directions: Trace and **print** 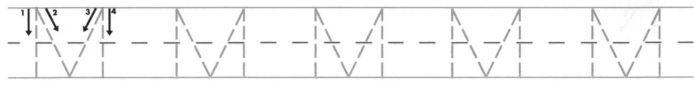 the letters.

UPPERCASE

lowercase

Directions: The pictures begin with the letter **Mm**.

Colour the pictures.

Letter Nn

Directions: Trace and **print**  the letters.

UPPERCASE

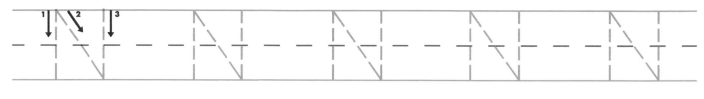

lowercase

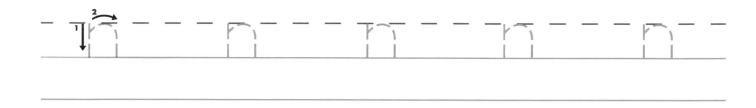

Directions: The pictures begin with the letter **Nn**.

Colour  the pictures.

Letter Oo

Directions: Trace and **print** 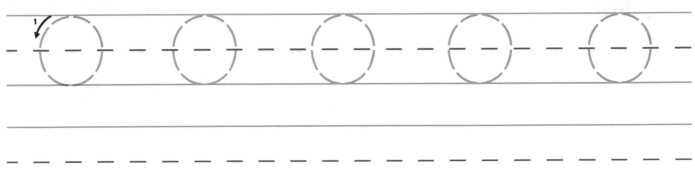 the letters.

UPPERCASE

lowercase

Directions: The pictures begin with the letter **Oo**.

Colour  the pictures.

Letter Pp

Directions: Trace and **print**  the letters.

UPPERCASE

lowercase

Directions: The pictures begin with the letter **Pp**.

Colour  the pictures.

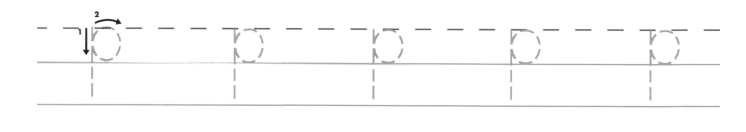

Letter Qq

Directions: Trace and **print** 🖊 the letters.

UPPERCASE

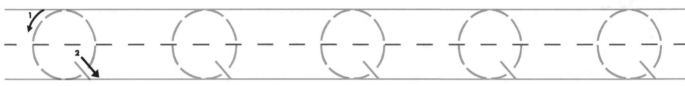

lowercase

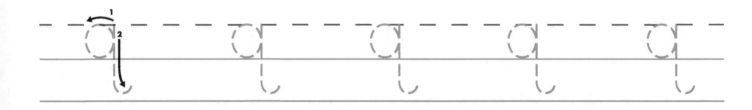

Directions: The pictures begin with the letter **Qq**.
Colour 🖍 the pictures.

Letter Rr

Directions: Trace and **print** the letters.

UPPERCASE

lowercase

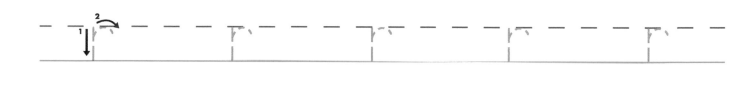

Directions: The pictures begin with the letter **Rr**.

Colour  the pictures.

Letter Ss

Directions: **Trace** and **print**  the letters.

UPPERCASE

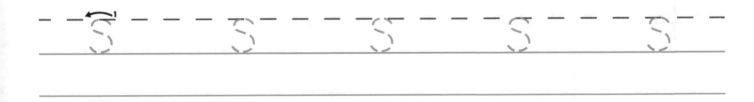

lowercase

Directions: The pictures begin with the letter **Ss.**

Colour the pictures.

Letter Tt

Directions: Trace and **print**  the letters.

UPPERCASE

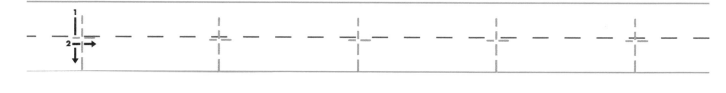

lowercase

Directions: The pictures begin with the letter **Tt**.

Colour  the pictures.

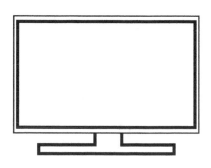

Letter Uu

Directions: Trace and **print** 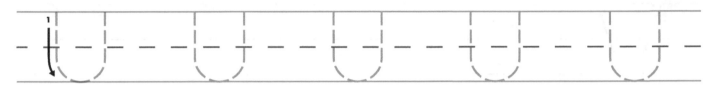 the letters.

UPPERCASE

lowercase

Directions: The pictures begin with the letter **Uu**.

Colour  the pictures.

Letter Vv

Directions: Trace and **print** 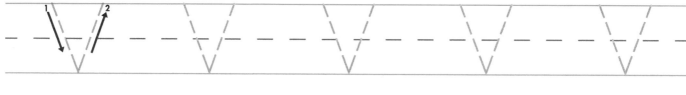 the letters.

UPPERCASE

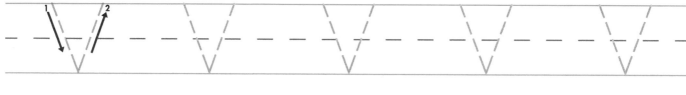

lowercase

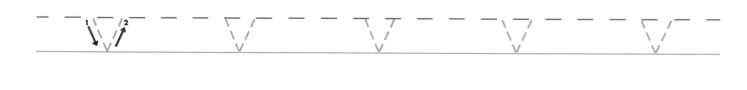

Directions: The pictures begin with the letter **Vv**.

Colour  the pictures.

Letter Ww

Directions: Trace and **print**  the letters.

UPPERCASE

lowercase

Directions: The pictures begin with the letter **Ww**.

Colour  the pictures.

Letter Xx

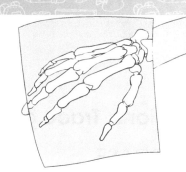

Directions: Trace and **print** 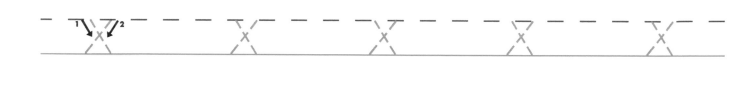 the letters.

UPPERCASE

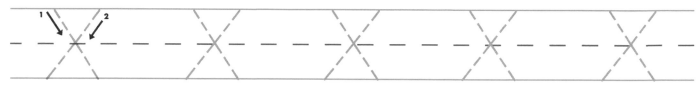

lowercase

Directions: The pictures begin or end with the letter **Xx**.

Colour the pictures.

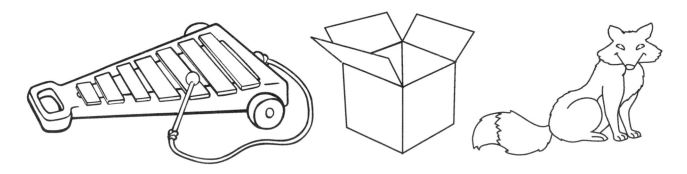

Letter Yy

Directions: Trace and **print** 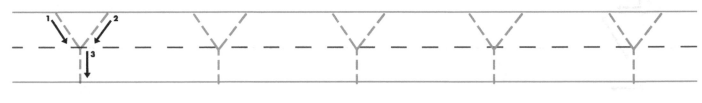 the letters.

UPPERCASE

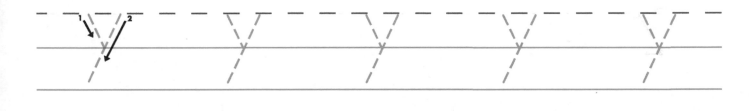

lowercase

Directions: The pictures begin with the letter **Yy**.

Colour  the pictures.

Letter Zz

Directions: **Trace** and **print**  the letters.

UPPERCASE

lowercase

Directions: The pictures begin with the letter **Zz**.

Colour the pictures.

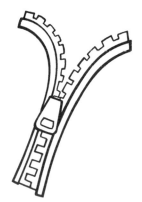

Letter Recognition Aa, Bb, Cc

Directions: Circle the letters in each row that match the first letter.

A	N	(A)	V	(A)
a	b	a	c	a
B	B	C	B	A
b	d	a	b	a
C	O	C	D	C
c	a	c	c	o

Letter Recognition Dd, Ee, Ff

Directions: Circle  the letters in each row that match the first letter.

D	B	G	D	B
d	b	d	a	d
E	H	F	E	E
e	e	a	b	e
F	E	F	E	A
f	t	f	l	o

Letter Recognition Gg, Hh, Ii

Directions: Circle  the letters in each row that match the first letter.

G	C	G	O	B
g	g	p	q	g
H	E	F	H	I
h	d	n	b	h
I	H	I	L	A
i	t	i	l	i

Name _____

Letter Recognition Jj, Kk, Ll

Directions: Circle  the letters in each row that match the first letter.

J	J	U	L	J
j	g	j	q	i
K	N	F	H	K
k	l	h	k	b
L	J	I	L	U
l	t	i	l	i

Complete Canadian Reading Kindergarten   130   Letter Recognition

Letter Recognition Mm, Nn, Oo

Directions: Circle the letters in each row that match the first letter.

M	H	M	n	L
m	M	a	m	n
N	M	N	m	N
n	n	m	a	n
O	O	D	B	O
o	a	O	c	o

Letter Recognition Pp, Qq, Rr

Directions: Circle the letters in each row that match the first letter.

P	D	P	O	b
p	p	d	q	b
Q	O	Q	G	Q
q	p	q	d	b
R	R	B	P	R
r	r	n	m	r

Letter Recognition Ss, Tt, Uu

Directions: Circle  the letters in each row that match the first letter.

S	P	S	B	S
s	o	a	s	e
T	I	P	L	T
t	f	l	t	i
U	U	D	U	O
u	u	n	m	n

Letter Recognition Vv, Ww, Xx

Directions: Circle the letters in each row that match the first letter.

V	W	V	A	N
V	W	X	V	y
W	V	M	A	W
w	W	v	x	m
X	Y	X	V	K
x	y	k	x	z

Letter Recognition Yy, Zz

Directions: Circle the letters in each row that match the first letter.

Y	W	Y	V	X
y	W	X	V	y
Z	N	M	Z	W
z	n	z	x	m

Name _____

Review Uppercase Letters

Directions: Print  the missing uppercase letters to complete the alphabet.

Review Lowercase Letters

Directions: Print  the missing lowercase letters to complete the alphabet.

Alphabet Review

Directions: Trace  the UPPERCASE letters. **Print** the missing UPPERCASE letters.

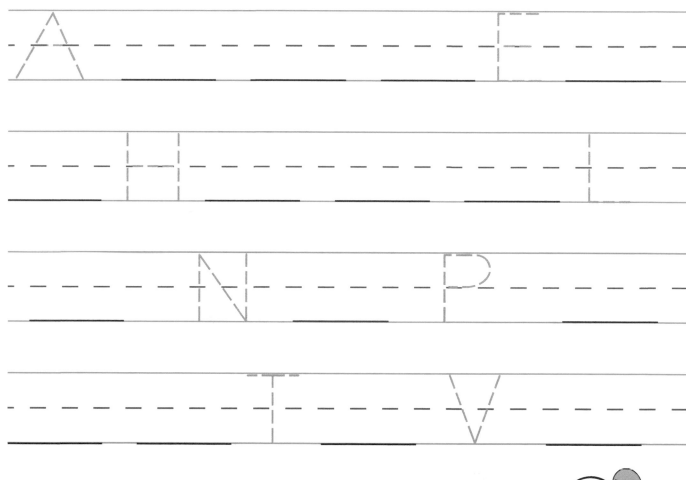

A _ _ _ _ _ _ _ _ F

_ _ H _ _ _ _ _ _ L

_ _ N _ _ P _ _ _

_ _ _ _ T _ V _ _

X _ Z _ _ _ _

Alphabet Review

Directions: Trace the lowercase letters. **Print** the missing lowercase letters.

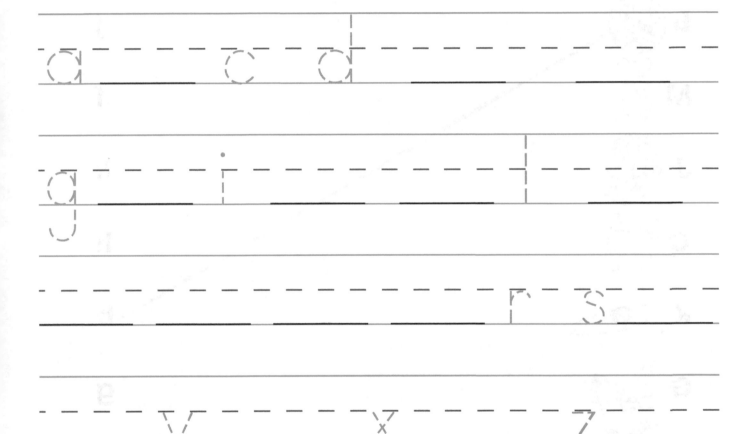

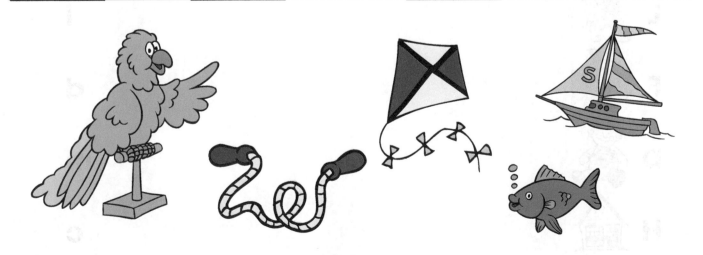

Letter Match

Directions: Draw 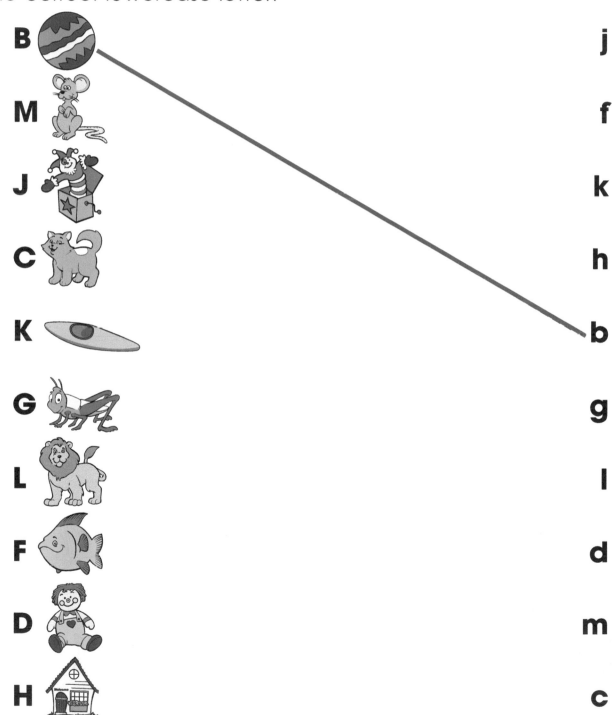 a line to match each UPPERCASE letter with the correct lowercase letter.

B	j
M	f
J	k
C	h
K	b
G	g
L	l
F	d
D	m
H	c

Letter Recognition

Letter Match

Directions: Draw 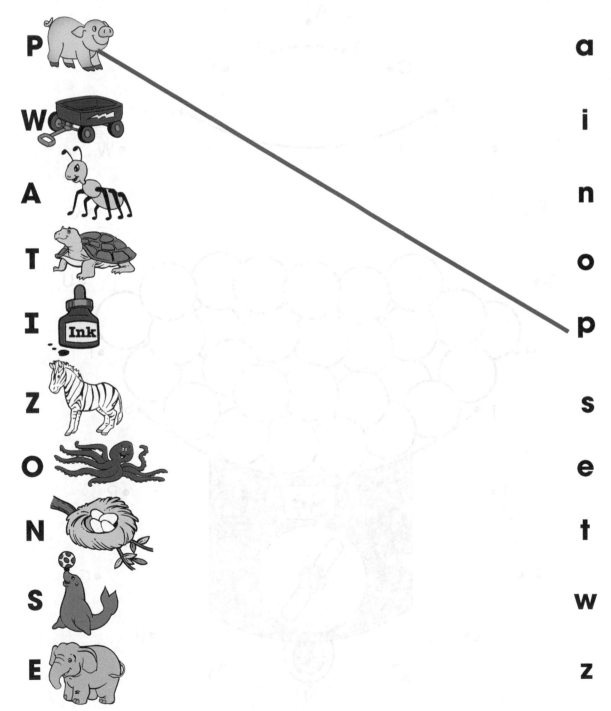 a line to match each UPPERCASE letter with the correct lowercase letter.

P   a

W   i

A   n

T   o

I   p

Z   s

O   e

N   t

S   w

E   z

Great Gumballs!

Directions: Connect 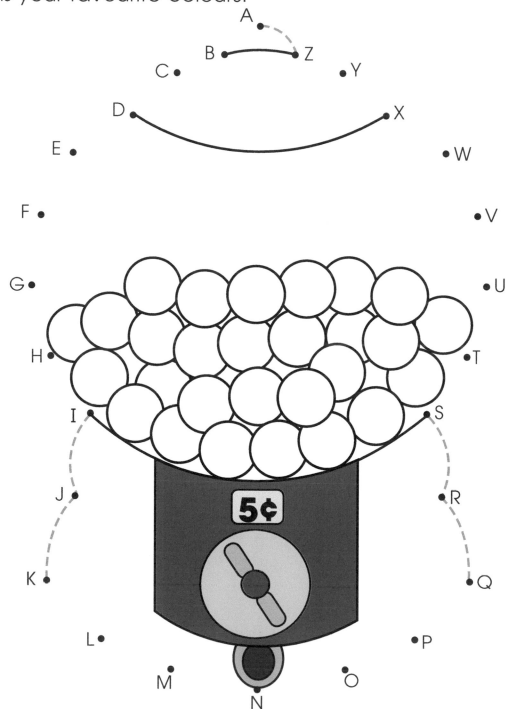 the dots from **A** to **Z**. **Colour** the gumballs your favourite colours!

142

Letter Recognition

Book Bonanza

Directions: Colour each picture that begins with the sound of **Bb**. **Cut out** and **glue** the **Bb** pictures on the book.

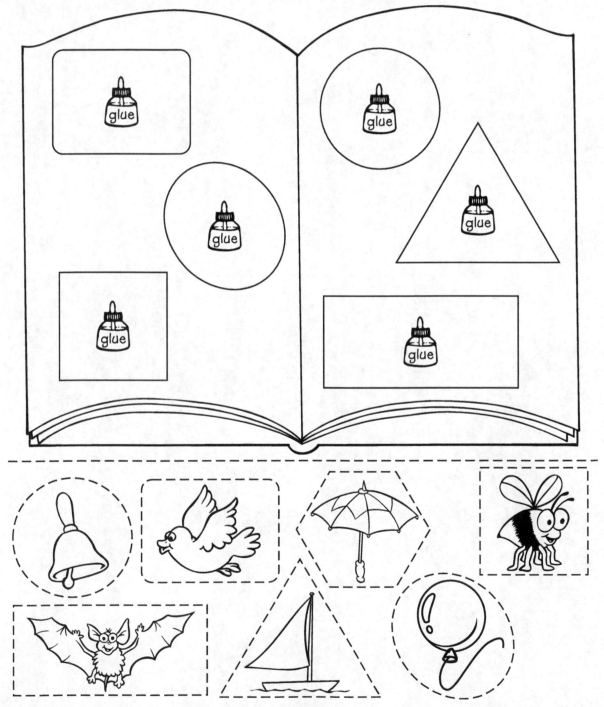

Buddy's Basket

Buddy is putting things in his basket.
He wants only things that begin with **Bb**.

Directions: Colour  the pictures of things that begin with **Bb**.

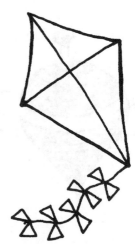

How many things will Buddy put in his basket? _____

Todd's Toy Box

Todd's toy box only has toys that begin with **Tt**. Look at the toys below. Which ones belong in the box?

Directions: Draw  lines from those toys to the box.

Tiger's T-Shirts

Help Tiger decide which T-shirts to buy.

Directions: Colour only the T-shirts with pictures that begin with the sound of **Tt**.

Letters Bb and Tt

Directions: Circle  the beginning sound for each picture.

10

b t   b t   b t

b t   b t   b t

b t   b t   b t

Soap Suds

Directions: Trace 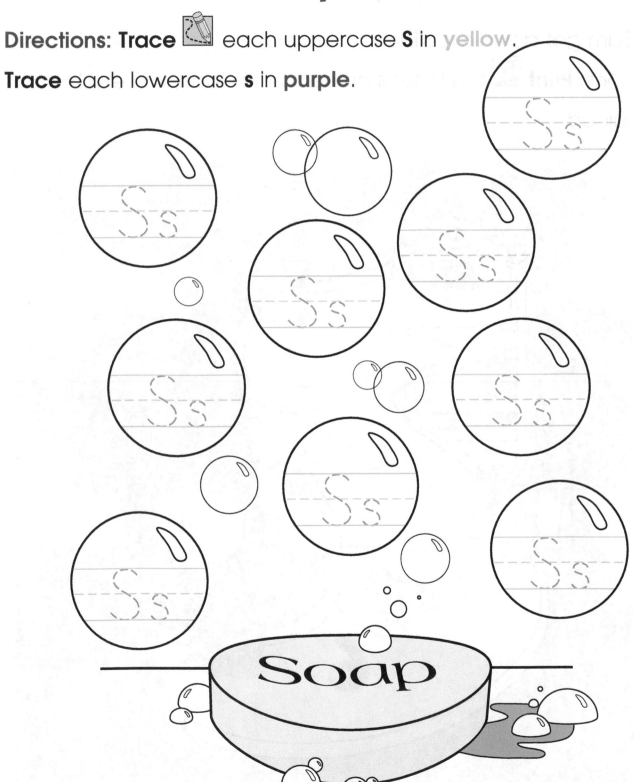 each uppercase **S** in yellow.

Trace each lowercase **s** in **purple**.

149

Name _____

A Super Slide

Help Sam get down the slide.

Directions: Print  the letter **s** on each line. Then, say each word aloud.

Where's the Cat?

Help Cara find her cat.

Directions: Colour  the pictures that begin

with **Cc** to make a path for Cara to follow.

Crazy Caterpillar

Give the caterpillar some spots.

Directions: Say the name of each picture. If the picture name begins with the same sound as **caterpillar, circle**  the picture to make a spot.

152

Name _____

Letters Cc and Ss

Directions: Trace the letters. **Colour** the picture in each box that begins with the sound of the letter.

Mouse Magic

Help Michael Mouse perform magic.

Directions: Colour  only the pictures that begin with the sound of **Mm**.

Amazing Maze

Maggie Moose wants to get to her mouse.

Directions: Colour  the pictures that begin with **Mm** to make a path for her.

Dixie's Drawings

Dixie drew pictures of things that begin

with **Dd**. Look at the pictures below.

Directions: Circle the ones that Dixie drew.

Dudley's Doghouse

Help Dudley find a **Dd** picture for each doghouse.

Directions: Colour and **cut out** each picture that begins with the sound of **Dd**. **Glue** each picture on a doghouse.

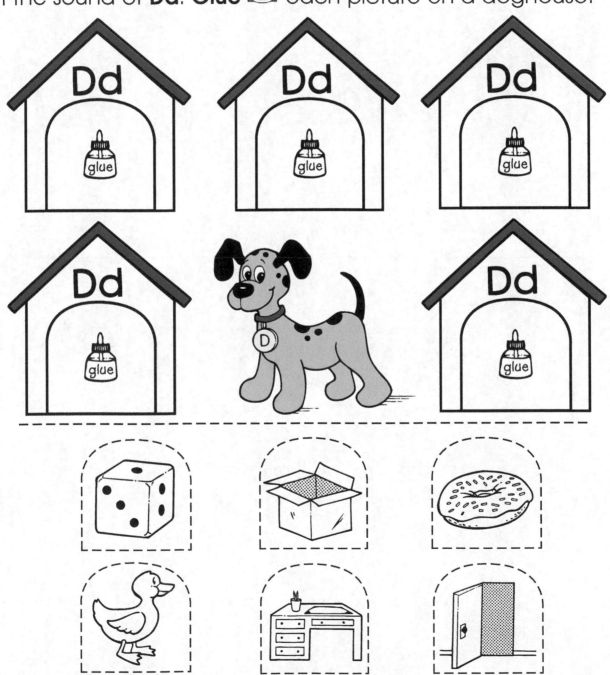

Name _____

Consonant Review

Directions: Print  the beginning sound for each picture.

_____ _____ _____ _____

- - - - - - - - - - - - - - - - - - - -

_____ _____ _____ _____

_____ _____ _____ _____

- - - - - - - - - - - - - - - - - - - -

_____ _____ _____ _____

_____ _____ _____ _____

- - - - - - - - - - - - - - - - - - - -

_____ _____ _____ _____

Wonderful Wagon

The wagon can carry only pictures whose names begin with the sound of **Ww**.

Directions: **Colour** these pictures.

Waldo's Wall

Waldo is building a wall. Look at the pictures on it.

Directions: Colour  the pictures that begin with **Ww**.

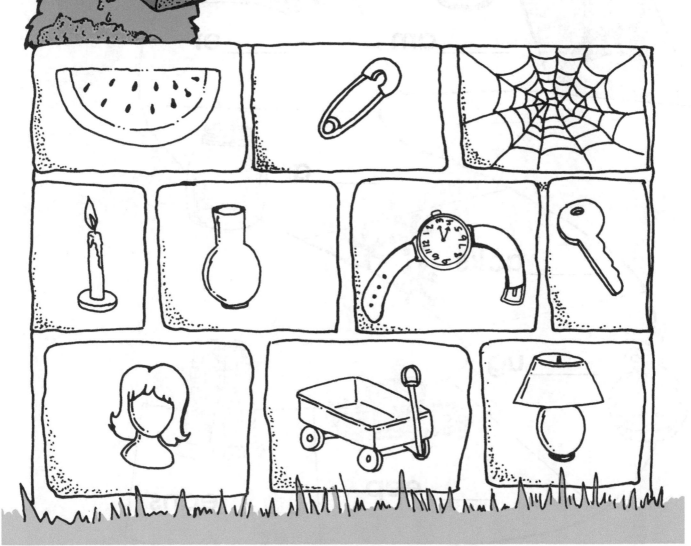

Jump, Jake, Jump!

Help Jake jump along the path.

Directions: Print 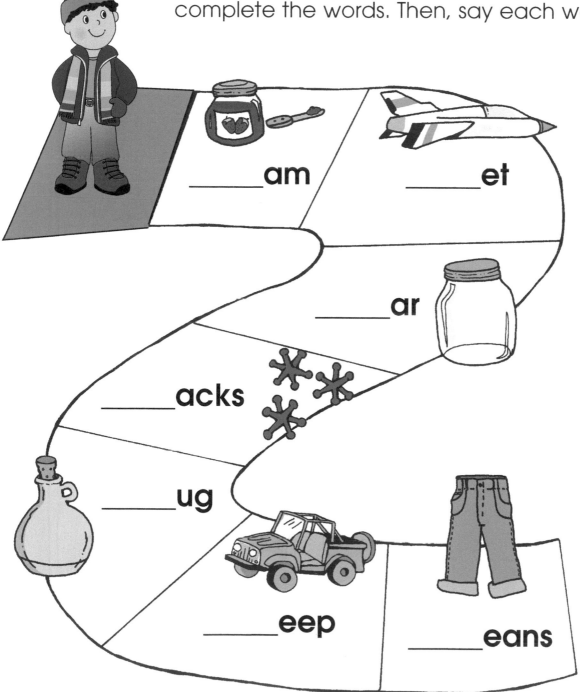 the letter **j** on the lines to complete the words. Then, say each word aloud.

_____am

_____et

_____ar

_____acks

_____ug

_____eep

_____eans

Jumping Jacks

Directions: Colour  each picture that begins with the sound of **Jj**. **Cut out** and **glue** the **Jj** pictures on the circles.

Letters Ww and Jj

Directions: Circle the beginning sound for each picture.

Colour the pictures.

w   j   w   j   w   j

w   j   w   j   w   j

w   j   w   j   w   j

Fun Finds

These kids are looking for books that begin with **Ff**.

Directions: Draw a line from each kid to a book that has something on it beginning with **Ff**.

Funny Faces

Directions: Colour 🖍️ **and cut out** ✂️ each picture that begins with the sound of **Ff**. **Glue** 🧴 each picture on the fence.

Remarkable Rockets

Directions: Colour 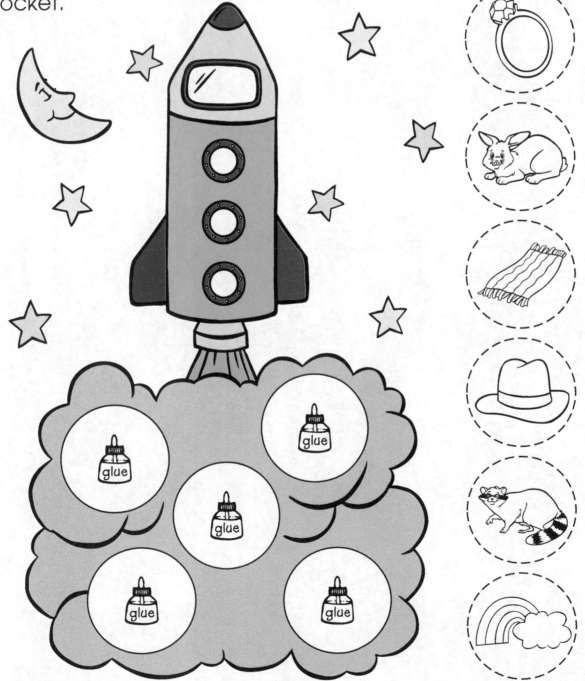 and **cut out** each picture that begins with the sound of **Rr. Glue** each picture on a circle under the rocket.

Rain, Rain, Go Away

Directions: Colour  the raindrops that have pictures that begin with **Rr**.

171

Pizza Party

Look at the picture.

Directions: Circle  the nine things that begin with **Pp**.

Plenty of Pepperoni

Directions: Colour and **cut out** each picture that begins with the sound of **Pp**. **Glue** each **Pp** picture on the pizza.

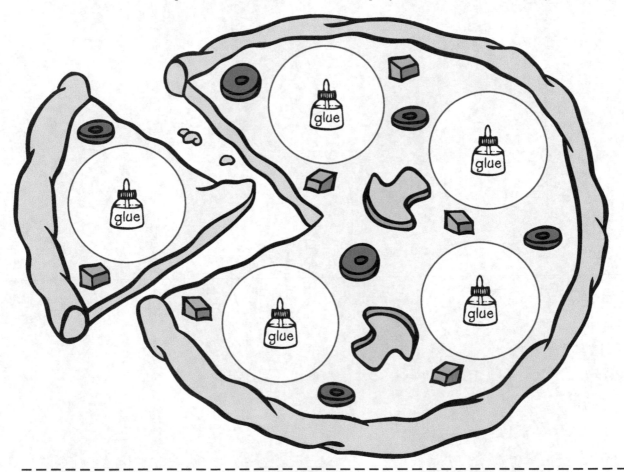

Home We Go!

Help Homer and his dog get home!

Directions: Colour the pictures that begin with the sound of **Hh**. Then, follow the path to Homer's house.

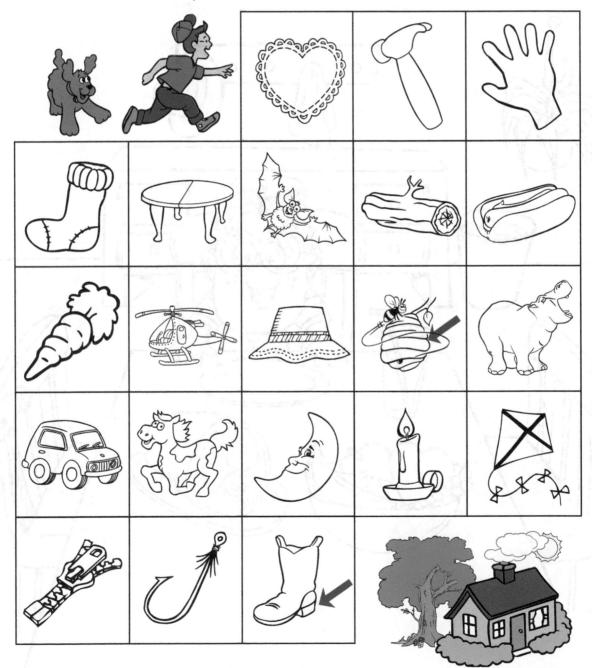

In Huey's House

Find the five **Hh** things in Huey's house.

Directions: Colour  them **red**. Then, colour the rest of the picture.

Nice Nests

Directions: Colour 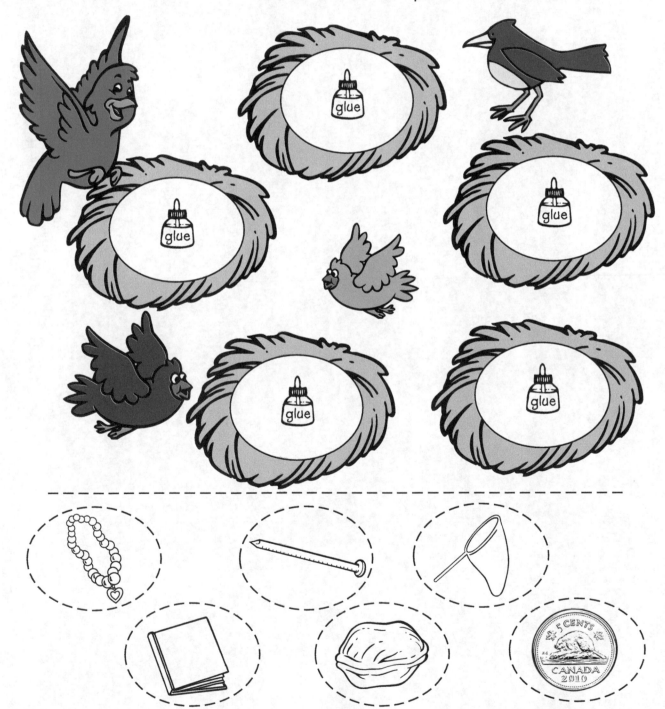 and **cut out** each picture that begins with the sound of **Nn**. **Glue** each **Nn** picture on a nest.

Handy Norman

Norman loves the letter **Nn**!

Directions: Draw  a line from each of Norman's hands to a picture of something that begins with **Nn**.

Name _____

Letters Hh and Nn

Directions: Colour 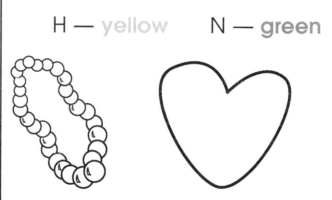 each picture the correct colour to match the beginning sound of each picture.

H — **red** N — yellow	H — orange N — **blue**

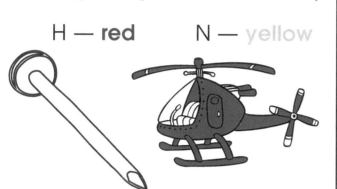   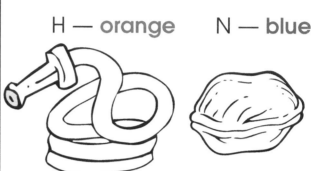

H — **green** N — **purple**	H — yellow N — green

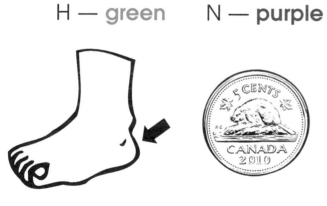   

H — **blue** N — **red**	H — **purple** N — orange

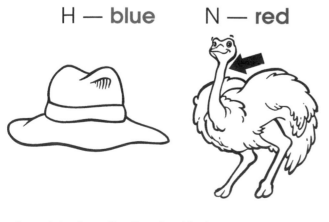   

Complete Canadian Reading Kindergarten

180

Consonant Sounds

King's Castle

Help the king colour the correct pictures for his castle.

Directions: Colour  each picture that begins with the sound of **Kk**.

181

Special Keys

Each monster has a key. The keys will open only chests that have pictures of things beginning with **Kk**.

Directions: Circle  the chests the keys will open.

A Valentine Treat

Six things that begin with **Vv** are hidden in the picture below.

Directions: Find them and **colour** them **brown**. Then, **colour** the rest of the picture.

Very Vivid V's

Directions: Draw  a line from **Vv** to each picture that begins with the sound of **Vv**. Then, **colour** the **Vv** pictures.

Name _____

Consonant Review

Directions: Print  the beginning sound for each picture in the boxes.

m

Light It Up!

Directions: Draw  a line from the light to each picture that begins with the sound of **Ll**. Then, **colour** the **Ll** pictures.

Lovely Leaves

These squirrels are watching the leaves fall.

Directions: Look at the picture on each leaf. If it begins with **Ll**,

colour the leaf yellow. If it does not, **colour** the leaf orange.

How many leaves are yellow? _____

How many leaves are orange? _____

A Great Garden of G's

Directions: Print  **Gg** under each picture that begins with the sound of **Gg. Colour** the **Gg** pictures.

Name _____

Help Gus

Look at each picture. Say its name.

Directions: Colour  the pictures that begin with **Gg**.

A Colourful Quilt

Directions: If the picture inside the quilt square begins with **Qq**, **colour** it orange. If it does not, **colour** it purple.

A Q Quilt

Directions: Colour  and **cut out** each picture that begins with the sound of **Qq**. **Glue** each **Qq** picture on the quilt. **Trace** the letters.

Yvette's Yo-Yos

Directions: Draw  a line from the girl to each picture that begins with the sound of **Yy**. **Colour** the **Yy** pictures.

Yolanda's Picture Chart

Help Yolanda finish her picture chart.

Directions: Print  **y** on the lines to complete the words. Then, say each word aloud.

y̲ o-yo

____ olk

____ ak

____ ard

____ arn

____ ellow

At the Zoo

Let's visit the zoo.

Directions: Circle  things hidden in the picture that begin with

Zz.

Zep Zebra's Zoo

Zep Zebra likes living in the zoo.

Directions: Colour  each picture that begins with the sound of **Zz**.

Consonant Review

Say the name of each picture.

Directions: Print the letter that makes the beginning sound.

 _ _ _ _ _

 _ _ _ _ _

 _ _ _ _ _

 _ _ _ _ _

 _ _ _ _ _

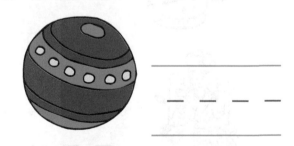 _ _ _ _ _

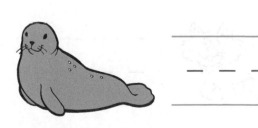 _ _ _ _ _

 _ _ _ _ _

Consonant Review

Say the name of each picture.

Directions: Print ✏️ the letter that makes the beginning sound.

Name _____

Consonant Review

Say the name of each picture.

Directions: Print the letter that makes the beginning sound.

Amazing A's

Directions: Draw 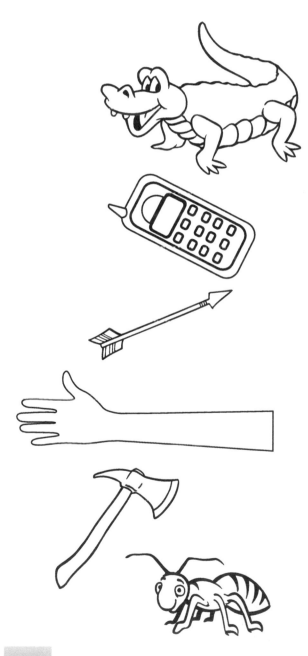 a line from each apple to a picture that begins with the sound of **Aa**. Draw an **X** on the picture that does **not** belong. **Colour** the **Aa** pictures.

Andy's Pictures

Help Andy label his pictures below and on page 202.

Directions: Trace  the words. Then, say the words aloud. Listen to the sound that **a** makes.

ant

axe

Andy's Pictures

In the Attic

Directions: Find the pictures of things that have the short **Aa** sound in them. **Colour**  them yellow. Then, **colour** the rest of the picture.

"Egg-ceptional" E!

Directions: Draw  a line from each egg to a picture that begins with the sound of **Ee**. Draw an **X** on the picture that does **not** belong.

In Elmo's Room

Below and on page 206 are some things that are in Elmo's room.

They have the **e** sound in them.

Directions: Trace  the words. Then, say the words aloud. Listen

to the sound that **e** makes.

bed

vest

In Elmo's Room

pen

desk

Fun on a Sled

Help the monsters ride their sled down the hill.

Directions: Print  **e** on the lines to complete the words. Then, say the words aloud.

b_e_ll

t____nt

d____sk

h____n

n____st

v____st

dr____ss

Name _____

Vowel Review

Say the name of each picture.

Directions: Print ✏️ the letter that makes the beginning sound.

Vowel Sounds

An Ii Igloo

Help build the igloo with **Ii** pictures.

Directions: Colour  and **cut out** each picture that begins with the sound of **Ii**. **Glue** each **Ii** picture on the igloo.

Izzy's Gifts

Look at Izzy's birthday gifts! They have the **i** sound in them.

Directions: Trace  the words below and on page 212. Then, say the words aloud. Listen to the sound that **i** makes.

dish   mitt

Name _____

Izzy's Gifts

pig

fish

Make a Wish

The animals are at a wishing well. Find out what each one is hoping to get.

Directions: Print  **i** on the lines to complete each word. Then, say the words aloud.

p__i__g

m____tt

f____sh

d____sh

Oo Animal Search

Can you find the **Oo** animals?

Directions: Trace  each **Oo**. **Colour**  the animals that begin

with the sound of **Oo**.

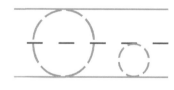

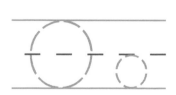

Olive's Bedroom

What things are in Olive's bedroom? They have the **o** sound in them.

Directions: Trace  the words below and on page 216. Then,

say the words aloud. Listen to the sound that **o** makes.

sock

clock

Olive's Bedroom

top

doll

Otter Hop

Help Olive and her friend Otto hop across the pond.

Directions: Write  the missing **o** for each word. Then, say the words aloud.

l__o__g

t_____p

b_____x

m_____p

f_____x

d_____g

r___ck

Unusual Umbrellas

Directions: Draw  a line from each child to a picture that begins with the sound of **Uu**.

Ug's Puppets

Ug collects puppets. Some of his puppets are shown below and on page 220.

Directions: Trace  the words.

Then, say the words aloud.

Listen to the sound that

u makes.

bug

cub

Ug's Puppets

Name _____

Fun in the Sun

Find four things that have the short **Uu** sound in the scene below.

Directions: Colour  them yellow. Then, **colour** the rest of the picture.

Vowel Sounds

221

Complete Canadian Reading Kindergarten

Name _____

Vowel Sounds

Look at each picture.

Directions: Draw 🖊️ a line to the letter that makes the same vowel sound.

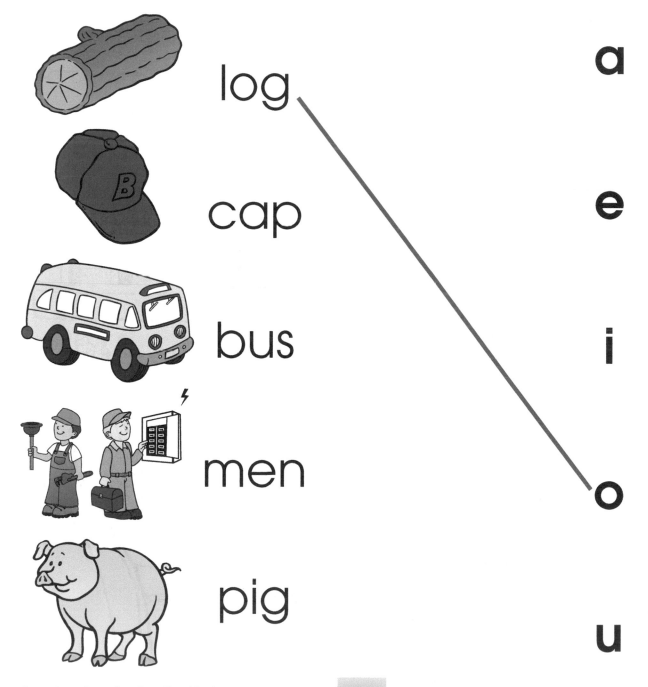

log

cap

bus

men

pig

a

e

i

o

u

Complete Canadian Reading Kindergarten   222   Vowel Sounds

Animal Snapshots

The monsters took pictures of some animals. Label the pictures.

Directions: Write  **a, e, i, o, or u on each line.**

p__i__g

c____t

b____t

h____n

____nt

f____sh

d____g

fr____g

d____ck

At the Toy Shop

Look at the vowel at the beginning of each row.
Then, name the toys in the row.

Directions: Circle  the toys that have the matching

vowel sound.

Riddle Time

Read the riddles.

Directions: Print the answers. Use the words at the bottom of the page.

This can spin fast. _____ **top** _____

This can ring and ring. _____

This is a soft pet. _____

This holds food. _____

This is very hot. _____

sun

bell

cat

dish

top

Animal Art

Read the words below and on page 227.

Directions: Draw ✏️ pictures to match.

a big bus

a small doll

Animal Art

six bugs

ten rocks

Pet Shop Game

Directions: Cut out  the game board on pages 229 and 231 .

Tape the game board together at the "short **o**."

This is a game for two players. Ask a parent or a friend to play with you. You will need one coin and two markers.

Directions for the Game:

1. Each player places a marker on the space marked **Start**.

2. Take turns flipping the coin and moving your marker along the game board. If the coin lands heads up, move one space. If it lands tails up, move two spaces.

3. If a player lands on a short vowel, he or she says a word that has that sound and moves an extra space forward.

4. If a player lands on a picture, he or she names it and tells which short vowel is in the word. Then, the player moves an extra space forward.

5. The first player to reach the puppies in the pet shop wins.

Pet Shop Game Board

Start

short **a**

short **i**

short **e**

Pet Shop Game Board

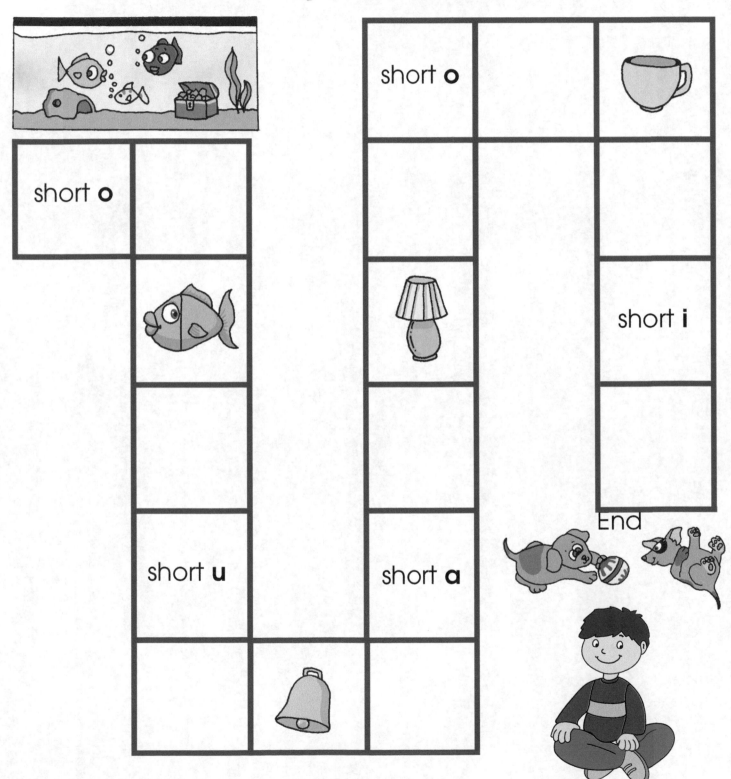

Rhyming Pairs

Words that have the same ending sounds are called **rhyming** words.

Directions: Circle  the pairs that rhyme.

map   nest   dog   frog

hat   bat   kite   mop

can   fan   rat   pig

Rhyming Pairs

Words that have the same ending sounds are called **rhyming** words.

Directions: Circle the pairs that rhyme.

nose   hose   beet   feet

star   jar   box   fox

dish   fish   cake   cap

Rhyming Pairs

Think of a word that rhymes with each picture.

Directions: Draw  a picture. **Print** the word.

Rhyming Pairs

Think of a word that rhymes with each picture.

Directions: Draw 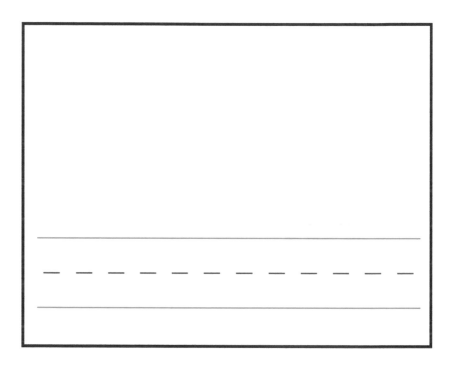a picture. **Print** the word.

Rhyming Word Picture Cards

Directions: Cut out ✂ the pictures below and on page 239. Match the rhyming words.

cat

man

car

boy

bee

bun

wig

frog

hen

Rhyming Word Picture Cards

hat	pan	jar

toy	tree	sun

pig	dog	pen

Rhyme Time

Read the poem. Read the questions.

Directions: Circle the correct answers.

Jack and Jill went up the hill,
To fetch a pail of water.
Jack fell down and broke his crown,
And Jill came tumbling after.

◆ Who went up the hill?

◆ What were they going to fetch?

◆ Who fell down?

Word Recognition: Colours

Directions: Colour  each picture the correct colour.

red shirt

yellow ball

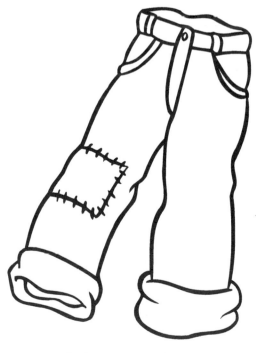

blue pants

green car

Word Recognition: Colours

Directions: Colour 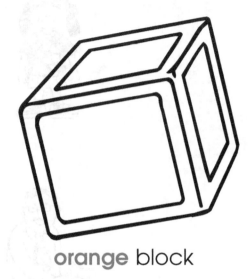 each picture the correct colour.

orange block

pink pig

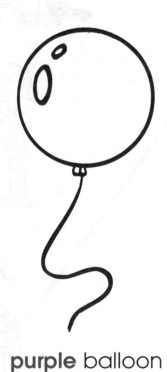

purple balloon

brown bear

Word Recognition: People

Directions: Draw 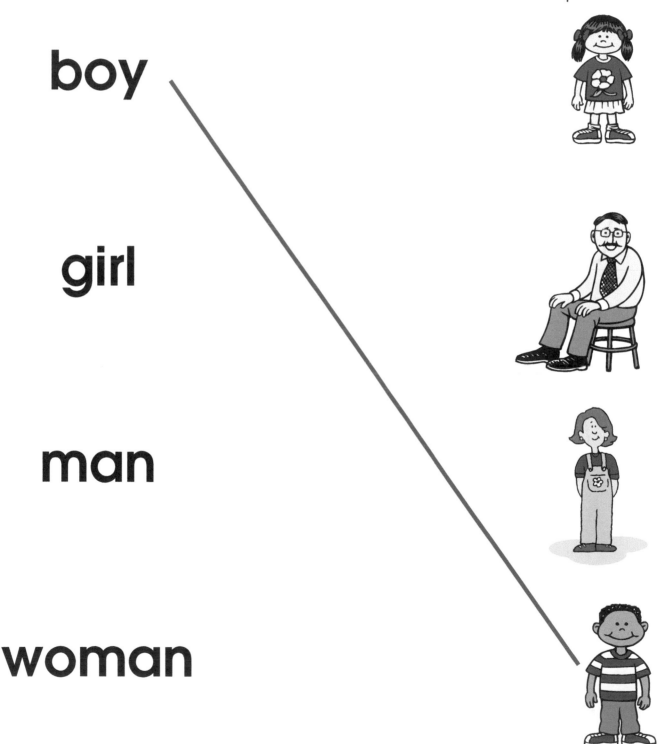 a line to match each word with its picture.

boy

girl

man

woman

Word Recognition: Things

Directions: Draw  a line to match each word with its picture.

cat

flower

car

tree

Word Recognition: Things

Directions: Draw  a line to match each word with its picture.

ball

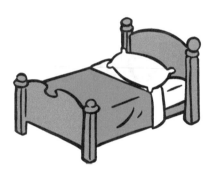

apple

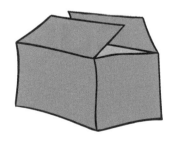

bed

box

Word Recognition: Action Words

Directions: Draw  a line to match the action word with the person doing that action.

walk

run

talk

eat

Name _____

Word Recognition: Action Words

Directions: Draw  a line to match the action word with the person doing that action.

play

ride

sit

cook

Word Recognition: Descriptions

Directions: Draw  a line to match each word with its picture.

tall

short

old

big

Word Recognition: Descriptions

Directions: Draw a line to match each word with its picture.

little

happy

sad

funny

Cool Countdown

Directions: Write  the numbers **1**, **2**, **3**, and **4** to show the correct order. **Colour** 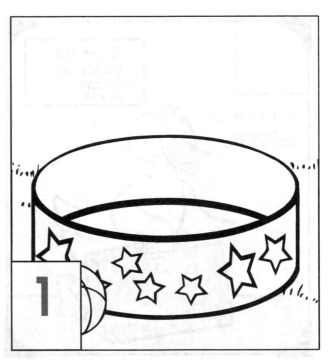 the pictures.

Ducky Destination

Directions: Help Ducky have a great vacation. **Print** the
numbers **1**, **2**, **3**, and **4** to show the correct order.

What Comes Next?

Directions: Colour  the first picture in each row. **Circle** and

colour the picture that comes **next** in the story.

What Comes First?

Directions: Circle  the picture in each row that shows what happened **first**. Colour the pictures.

What Comes Last?

Directions: Circle  the picture in each row that shows what happened **last. Colour** the pictures.

What Comes First?

Directions: Circle  the picture in each row that shows what happened **first. Colour** the pictures.

Picture Order

Directions: Colour  the pictures. **Cut out** the pictures in each row and put them in the order to show what comes first, second, and third.

What Comes Last?

Directions: Circle 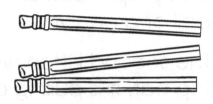 the picture in each row that shows what happened **last. Colour** the pictures.

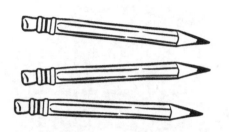

Name _____

What Comes Last?

Directions: Circle 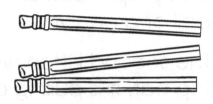 the picture in each row that shows what happened **last. Colour**  the pictures.

 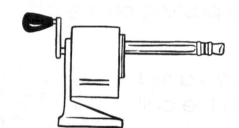

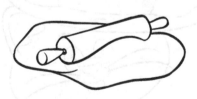 

  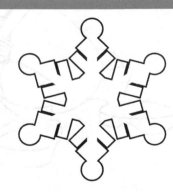

Name _____

What Comes Last?

Directions: Circle 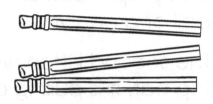 the picture in each row that shows what happened **last. Colour**  the pictures.

Sequencing

Complete Canadian Reading Kindergarten

The 3 Yellow Kittens

Directions: Colour  the 3 yellow kittens using the clues below.

The first kitten wears yellow bracelets and purple boots. It is pushing on the ball of green yarn.

The second kitten wears a red top hat. It is pulling on the ball of green yarn.

The third kitten is lounging on top of the ball of green yarn. It is wearing a blue T-shirt.

The Orchestra

Directions: Look at the picture below. **Colour**  the 3 violins **brown**. **Colour** the 3 flutes **silver**. **Colour** the drums **blue**. **Colour** the ladies' gowns **purple**. **Colour** the 2 cellos **yellow**. Colour the rest of the picture in a way that makes sense.

Stop Making Sense!

Directions: Look at the picture. A lot of silly things are happening! Draw an **X**  on all of the things that do **not** make sense.

Rainbow Clues

Directions: Follow the clues below. **Circle** your choices.

Find the object that is **brown** and **hard**.

Find the object that is yellow and **long**.

Find the object that is green and **sour**.

Find the object that is **blue** and **tiny**.

More Rainbow Clues

Directions: Follow the clues below. **Circle**  your choices.

Find the object that is orange and **sweet**.

Find the object that is yellow and **hard**.

Find the object that is **purple** and **smooth**.

   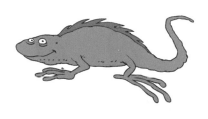

Find the object that is **black** and **sweet**.

Name _____

Colour It

Directions: Colour  the picture in each row that both words describe.

pink and cold

tall and sad

hot and hard

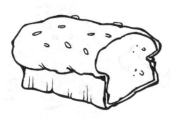   

dirty and soft

Picture Clues   **265**   Complete Canadian Reading Kindergarten

Colour It Again

Directions: Colour  the picture in each row that both words describe.

round and yellow

 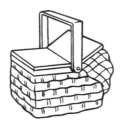  

scared and brown

wet and pointy

large and tired

Yellow Riddles

Directions: Find the picture that answers each riddle and **colour**  it yellow. **Colour** the other pictures in a way that makes sense.

I am yellow and I keep you **warm**. What am I?

I am yellow and **straight**. What am I ?

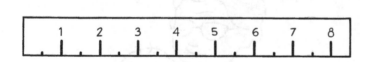  

I am yellow and **smell sweet**. What am I?

  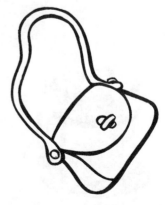

Grandma Gertie

Grandma Gertie loves flowers.

Directions: Use the clues below to find the perfect flower for

Grandma. **Circle**  your answer.

Grandma likes flowers that are pink.
She likes flowers that are tall.
She likes flowers that come with candy.

Jalen's Vacation

Jalen wants to go on vacation. Help him pick out the best spot for his trip. Read the clues below.

Jalen does not want to go to a cold place.
Jalen does not want to go to a beach.
Jalen wants to go to a place with games.

Directions: Circle the trip that Jalen should pick.

Find the Right Picture

Which picture goes with the sentence?

Directions: **Circle**  the correct picture.

Zelda is playing basketball
with her friends by the beach.

Find the Right Picture

Which picture goes with the sentence?

Directions: Circle the correct picture.

> Miles and Melvin are brothers who love sleeping outside during the summer. One day, they both lie down on a big hammock.

Find the Right Picture

Which picture goes with the sentence?

Directions: Circle  on the correct picture.

Orville and his mother play guitar together.

Dress for the Weather

Directions: Draw an **X**  on the children who are wearing the wrong clothes. **Colour** the children who are wearing the correct clothes.

Reality and Fantasy

Directions: Draw an **X** ✏️ on the 10 things in the picture that are **not** real.

Which Picture Is Missing?

Directions: Look at the pictures below. There is a picture missing.

Circle  the missing picture.

Which Picture Is Missing?

Directions: Look at the pictures below. There is a picture missing.

Circle the missing picture.

Which Picture Is Missing?

Directions: Look at the pictures below. There is a picture missing.

Circle 🖊️ the missing picture.

I'm Hungry!

Directions: Draw  a line to match each food item to the yummy meal it will make.

Which Items Do You Not Need?

Nathan is at the barber shop. He is getting his hair cut for the very first time.

Directions: Draw an **X** on the things the barber will **not** need to cut Nathan's hair.

Draw a picture of some other things he might need.

Which Items Do You Not Need?

Lauren and her dad want to play tennis.

Directions: Draw an **X** on the things they do **not** need to play tennis.

Draw a picture of some other things they might need.

Which Items Do You Not Need?

Julius and his brother want to help their mother get better. She has a terrible cold.

Directions: Draw an **X**  on the things they do **not** need to help her get better.

Draw a picture of some other things Julius and his brother might need.

Making Inferences — 281 — Complete Canadian Reading Kindergarten

Which Items Do You Not Need?

Lloyd is working at a bakery.

Directions: Draw an **X**  on the things he will **not** need to do his job well.

Draw pictures of some other things Lloyd might need.

Which Picture Is Missing From the Story?

Directions: Look at the pictures below. They start to make a story, but the last box is empty.

Which of these pictures helps to finish the story? **Circle** the picture.

Which Picture Is Missing From the Story?

Directions: Look at the pictures below. They start to make a story, but the last box is empty.

Which of these pictures helps to finish the story? **Circle**  the picture.

Name _____

What Will Happen Next?

Directions: Look at the picture above. Now, **circle**  the picture below that shows what happens next.

What Will Happen Next?

Directions: Look at the picture above. Now, **circle**  the picture below that shows what happens next.

Name _____

What's Next?

Directions: Look at the picture above. Now, **circle**  the picture below that shows what happens next.

287

Complete Canadian Reading Kindergarten

What's Next?

Directions: Look at the picture above. Now, **circle** the picture below that shows what happens next.

Reading Challenge - The First Day of School

The first day of school was fun. My new teacher's name is Miss Clark. Joy and Alan are in my class. At recess we played ball. I had pizza, pears, and milk for lunch. Miss Clark read a funny story about a little bear and his mother. I learned a lot today.

Directions: With an adult's help, read or listen to the story. Then answer the questions together. Circle the answers.

What words from the story begin with the same sound as  ?

fun   pizza   pears   new

Circle the picture that rhymes with **Joy**.

Which word means the same as **small**?

new   funny   little

What did the child in this story think about school?

It was funny. It was fun.

Who are Joy and Alan?

bears   classmates

Reading Challenge - Let's Go to School

There are many ways to go to school. Children who live nearby can walk. If they are late, they need to run. Some children ride the bus. Others like to ride their bikes. Parents can drive them in a car.

Directions: With an adult's help, read or listen to the story. Then answer the questions together. Circle the answers.

What words from the story have the sound of **i** that you hear in **ride**?

run   bikes   drive

Circle the picture that rhymes with **school**.

Which word is the opposite of **early**?

nearby   late   many

Why do some children run to school?

They are early.   They are late.

How do you get to school?

bus   car   walk   bike

Name _____

Reading Challenge - A Busy Day

We always get up early. Dad makes us breakfast. I feed Zip, the cat. Then, I walk to school. Mom and Dad go to work.

Directions: With an adult's help, read or listen to the story. Then answer the questions together. Circle the answers.

What words from the story have the same beginning sound as ?

we   early   walk   work

Circle the picture that rhymes with **walk**.

Which words in the story mean **Mom, Dad, and I together?**

we   I   us   mom

Why does everyone get up early?

for lunch   for breakfast

Why doesn't Zip go to school?

Zip is a teacher.   Zip is a cat.

Reading Challenge - Good Morning, Teacher

Our class is busy. We all say "Good morning" to the teacher. Then, we do our jobs. Rosa gives the plant some water. Ben counts the lunches. Tim gives us paper. We get out our books.

Directions: With an adult's help, read or listen to the story. Then answer the questions together. Circle the answers.

What words from the story begins with the blend you hear in  .

class   plant   counts

Circle the picture that rhymes with **plant**.

Which word in the story means **more than one book**?

paper   busy   books

What do the children do after they say "Good morning"?

They eat lunch.   They do their jobs.

How do you like to help at school?

Reading Challenge - School in Korea

What is school like in Korea? In Korea, school starts in March. Children carry their books in a backpack. They carry their school shoes in a cloth bag. They put them on when they go indoors.

Directions: With an adult's help, read or listen to the story. Then answer the questions together. Circle the answers.

What words from the story begins with the same sound as 🐑 sheep?

school   starts   shoes

What word in the story is made of two rhyming words?

school shoes   backpack

What word in the story is the name of a month?

indoors   Korea   March

Why do you think the children put on clean shoes in school?

Their feet hurt. Clean shoes keep the floors clean.

How do children in your school carry their books?

backpack   cloth bag   lunch bag

Reading Challenge - A Class Pet

Our teacher found a little lost rabbit on the playground. She was just a baby bunny when Mr. Bell found her. We fed her some milk. Now Bumper is grown up. She still comes to school every day.

Directions: With an adult's help, read or listen to the story. Then answer the questions together. Circle the answers.

What words in the story have the sound of **ou** that you hear in **pound**?

our   lost **found** grown playground now

Circle the picture that rhymes with **fed**.

What word in the story is another word for **rabbit**?

baby   bumper   bunny

Who is Mr. Bell?

He is a rabbit.   He is a teacher.

Who is Bumper?

She is a rabbit.   She is a teacher.

Name _____

Reading Challenge - School in Germany

Petra lives in Germany. It is the first day of school. Her parents give her a pretty paper cone to take to school. What is inside? Sweet things to eat for a sweet day!

Directions: With an adult's help, read or listen to the story. Then answer the questions together. Circle the answers.

What word from the story rhymes with ?

Petra   school   cone

Circle the picture that begins with the blend you hear at the beginning of **sweet**.

What word from the story is the opposite of **last**?

inside   first   pretty

What will make the first day sweet for Petra?

paper   sweet things to eat

Name some things that could be in Petra's cone.

shoes   paper   candy

Reading Challenge - A New Friend

Evan went to his school for the first time. He liked his teacher. But he felt all alone when it was time to play outside. Then, Nick asked Evan to kick the ball with him. Then, it was time to go inside. Nick sat by Evan on the rug to hear a story. Soon, it was time to go home. Nick said, "See you!" When Evan got home, he told his mother that he liked his new school a lot.

Directions: With an adult's help, read or listen to the story. Then answer the questions together. Circle the answers.

Find two words in the story that rhyme with **stick**.

first   kick   liked   Nick

Circle the picture that begins with the same sound you hear at the beginning of **home**.

Which word in the story is the opposite of **outside**?

new   home   inside

Why did Evan feel alone?

He was hungry.   It was his first day.

What did Nick do to help Evan?

Nick asked Evan to play ball.
Nick sat beside Evan. Nick said, "See you!"

Name _____

Reading Challenge - Bear Cubs

Bear cubs are born in winter. They may weigh less than a loaf of bread. In spring, the cubs and their mother go outside. As the cubs grow older, their mother teaches them how to find food. The cubs stay with their mother for a year or two. Then, the cubs go out on their own.

Directions: With an adult's help, read or listen to the story. Then answer the questions together. Circle the answers.

Circle the picture that begins with the blend you hear at the beginning of **grow**.

What words in the story rhyme with **day**?

cubs   may   stay   year

What word in the story means **a cold time of the year**?

outside   spring   winter

Why do you think the cubs stay with their mother for a year or two?

The cubs need time to grow and learn.
The cubs help their mother build a house.

How do you know that bear cubs are born very small?

They are born in winter.
They weigh less than a loaf of bread.

Name _____

Reading Challenge - Antarctic Penguins

Penguins are birds but they don't fly.
Penguins swim. Penguins lay eggs.
Most penguin chicks have fluffy feathers.
Penguins live in large groups.

Directions: With an adult's help, read or listen to the
story. Then answer the questions together. Circle the answers.

Circle the picture whose name begins with the blend you hear at
the beginning of **fluffy**.

What word from the story rhymes with **legs**?

eggs   birds   large

What word from the story means the same as **do not**?

have   don't   swim

Do all birds fly?

yes   no

What are baby penguins called?

pups   kittens   chicks

Complete Canadian Reading Kindergarten

Reading Comprehension

Reading Challenge - Canadian Animals on the Move

Some animals do not have a home in one place. They change their homes every day. They move from place to place. They look for food. Their home is where they stop to rest for the day. Deer and moose are always on the move.

Directions: With an adult's help, read or listen to the story. Then answer the questions together. Circle the answers.

What word in the story begins like ?

some   change   rest

What word in the story rhymes with **hear**?

home   deer   from

What word in the story is the opposite of **go**?

one   move   stop

Where is a deer's home?
where it stops to rest for the day
where it walks

Why do you think some animals move from place to place?

to look for food   to find a soft pillow

Reading Challenge - The Goat

Every Saturday, Grandma and I go bike riding. Grandma wears her straw hat. Last Saturday, we rode along the bike path to the fair. We went to see the farm animal show. We got to pet the goats. Grandma left her hat on the bike seat. A goat ate her hat!

Directions: With an adult's help, read or listen to the story. Then answer the questions together. Circle the answers.

Circle the picture that has the sound of **e** you hear in **pet**.

Circle the picture that names a word that rhymes with **goat**.

Which word in the story is a day of the week?

last   Saturday   show

Where does the bike path go?

to the fair   to the pet shop

Why will Grandma need a new hat?

A goat wore her hat.   A goat ate her hat.

Reading Challenge - Caring for Pets

Pets need food and water. Some pets need special homes. Some pets need exercise. Some pets need help keeping clean. All pets need love and care.

Directions: With an adult's help, read or listen to the story. Then answer the questions together. Circle the answers.

Circle the picture that has the sound of **e** you hear in **need**.

What word in the story rhymes with **gets**?

pets   exercise   care

What word from the story is the opposite of **dirty**?

special   help   clean

Name things that all pets need.

food special homes water love

Do you help care for a pet?

yes   no

Reading Challenge - Alberta Dinosaur Babies

In Alberta, a long ago, these dinosaurs built nests. They used mud and sand. They laid eggs. Plants kept the nests soft and warm. Baby dinosaurs hatched. The parents brought food. The babies grew. This dinosaur is Maiasaura. Its name means "good mother lizard." Can you see why?

Directions: With an adult's help, read or listen to the story. Then answer the questions together. Circle the answers.

Circle the picture that has the sound of **oo** you hear in **food**.

What words from the story rhyme with **blue**?

used   grew   good   you

What word from the story means **more than one dinosaur**?

dinosaurs   eggs   plants

What does **Maiasaura** mean?

good mother lizard   soft and warm

How was this dinosaur a good mother?
She made a soft nest.   She brought food.
She sang songs.

Reading Challenge - What Is a Bat?

A bat is a furry mammal. It is not a bird, but it can fly like one. It is the only mammal that can fly. Bats have very light bones. The bat's wings are made of smooth, thin skin. The wings are stretched between the bat's fingers.

Directions: With an adult's help, read or listen to the story. Then answer the questions together. Circle the answers.

What word from the story begins like **smile**?

wings   smooth   bat

What word from the story rhymes with **sings**?

size   thin   wings

What word from the story means **having fur**?

bird   smooth   furry

How is a bat different from all other mammals?

It is furry.   It can fly.

What is different about a bat's bones?

They are smooth. They are light.

Reading Challenge - Bluebird Boxes

    Our club is making bluebird boxes. Carmen's dad shows us how to nail the wood pieces together. We will put the boxes in the park. Bluebirds make their nests in tree holes. But there aren't enough tree holes, for them. Now, they can build nests in our boxes. My friends and I will check the boxes each week. We want to see if any bluebirds are using them. We will look for nests, eggs, and chicks.

Directions: With an adult's help, read or listen to the story. Then answer the questions together. Circle the answers.

Circle the picture that has the sound of **ai** that you hear in **nail**.

What word from the story rhymes with **filled**?

nail   build   holes

What word from the story is made up of two smaller words?

bluebird   boxes   eggs

What are bluebird boxes for?

Bluebirds can build nests in the boxes.

Bluebirds can eat them.

How will the children know if bluebirds are using the boxes?

They will check for nails and wood each week.

They will check for nests, eggs, and chicks each week.

Answer Key

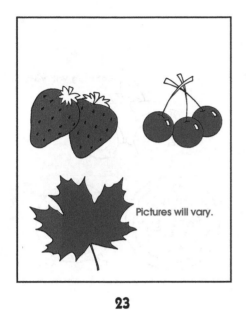

Pictures will vary.

23

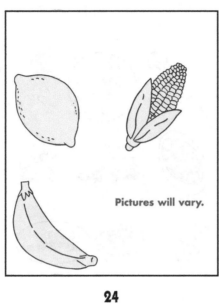

Pictures will vary.

24

25

Pictures will vary.

26

27

Pictures will vary.

28

29

30

Coloring will vary.

31

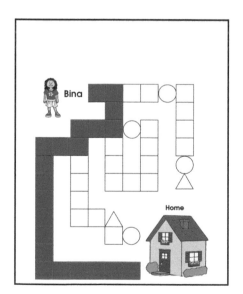

Bina

Home

32

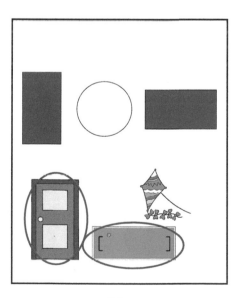

33

34

35

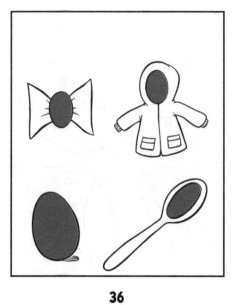

36

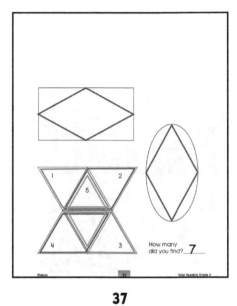

How many
did you find? 7

37

38

39

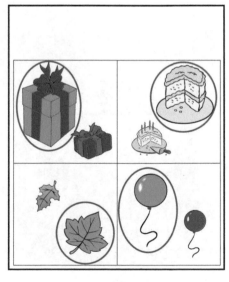

40

41

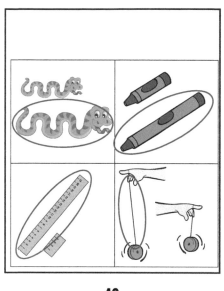

42

43

44

45

46

Drawings will vary but John should be shorter than Jill but taller than Jack.

47

How many tips are on the tallest moose's antlers? ___8___

How tall do you want to be? _____

48

49

51

What kinds of food do you eat on Thanksgiving Day?

52

53

54

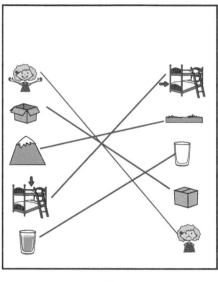

55

56

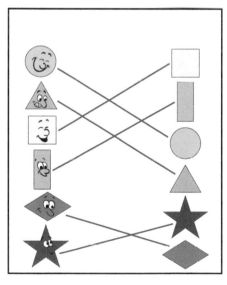

57

Colouring will vary.

58

Drawings will vary.

59

60

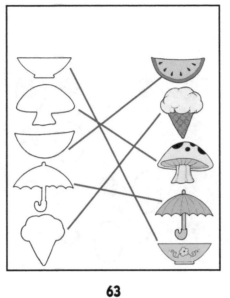

63

64

65

Answers will vary.

I am a hare!

I am a tortoise!

Most children will choose the hare.

66

Circle your favorite pair of shoes above.

67

311

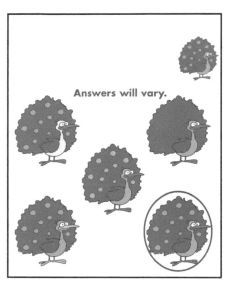

68

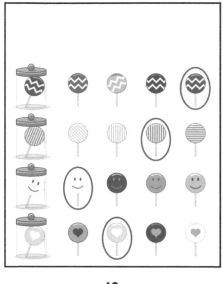

69

70

71

72

73

Which animal would you want for a pet? Why?
Answers will vary.

74

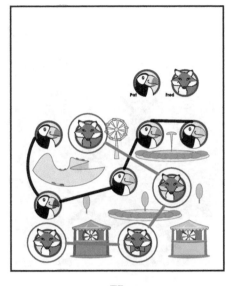

75

76

77

Which 3 things are on your hand?

Which 3 things would you need if you were sick?

Which 3 things are in the sky?

Which 3 things would you wear if you were hot?

78

79

Answer Key   313   Complete Canadian Reading Kindergarten

80

81

82

Answers will vary.

83

84

85

86

87

88

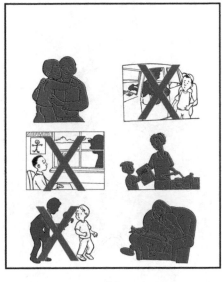

89

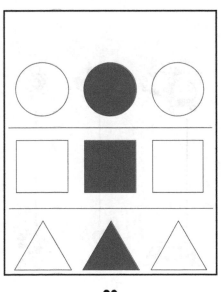

90

91

93

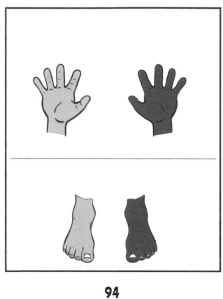

94

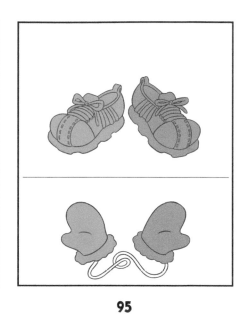

95

96

97

98

99

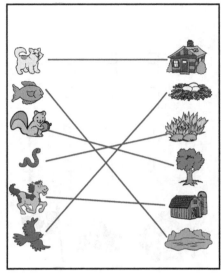

100

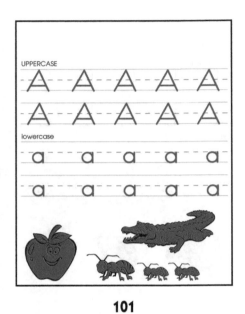

101

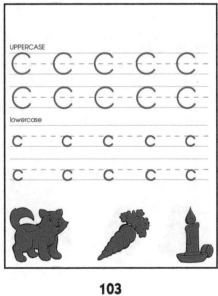

102

103

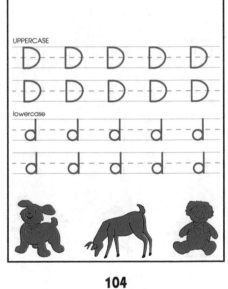

104

UPPERCASE

E E E E E
E E E E E

lowercase

e e e e e
e e e e e

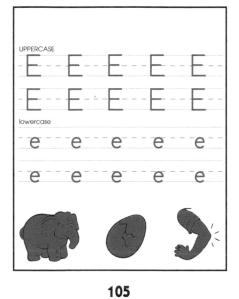

105

UPPERCASE

F F F F F
F F F F F

lowercase

f f f f f
f f f f f

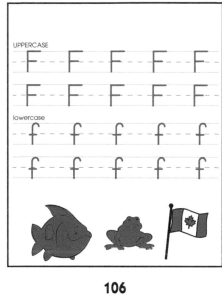

106

UPPERCASE

G G G G G
G G G G G

lowercase

g g g g g
g g g g g

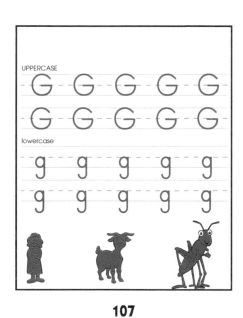

107

UPPERCASE

H H H H H
H H H H H

lowercase

h h h h h
h h h h h

108

UPPERCASE

I I I I I
I I I I I

lowercase

i i i i i
i i i i i

109

UPPERCASE

J J J J J
J J J J J

lowercase

j j j j j
j j j j j

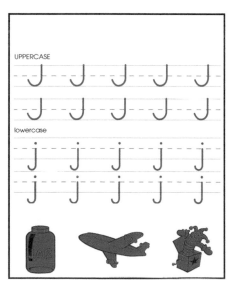

110

UPPERCASE

K K K K K
K K K K K

lowercase

k k k k k
k k k k k

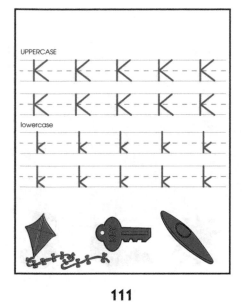

111

UPPERCASE

L L L L L
L L L L L

lowercase

l l l l l
l l l l l

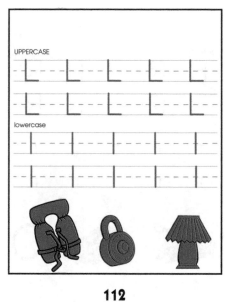

112

UPPERCASE

M M M M M
M M M M M

lowercase

m m m m m
m m m m m

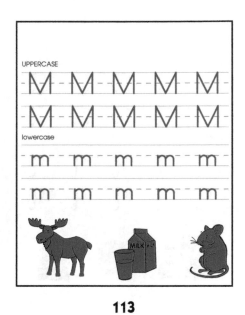

113

UPPERCASE

N N N N N
N N N N N

lowercase

n n n n n
n n n n n

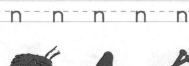

114

UPPERCASE

O O O O O
O O O O O

lowercase

o o o o o
o o o o o

115

UPPERCASE

P P P P P
P P P P P

lowercase

p p p p p
p p p p p

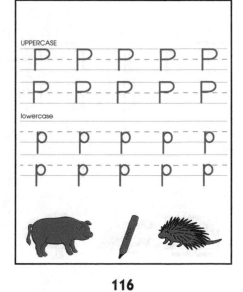

116

UPPERCASE

Q Q Q Q Q
Q Q Q Q Q

lowercase

q q q q q
q q q q q

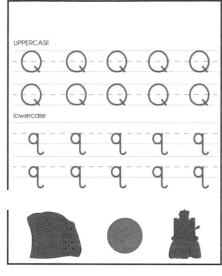

117

UPPERCASE

R R R R R
R R R R R

lowercase

r r r r r
r r r r r

118

UPPERCASE

S S S S S
S S S S S

lowercase

s s s s s
s s s s s

119

UPPERCASE

T T T T T
T T T T T

lowercase

t t t t t
t t t t t

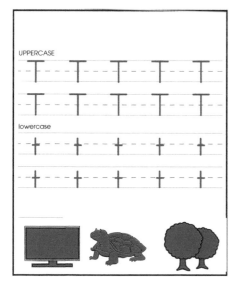

120

UPPERCASE

U U U U U
U U U U U

lowercase

u u u u u
u u u u u

121

UPPERCASE

V V V V V
V V V V V

lowercase

v v v v v
v v v v v

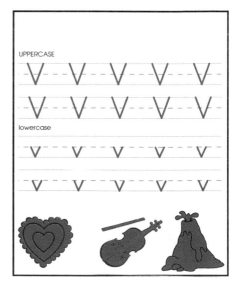

122

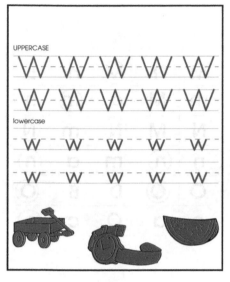

123

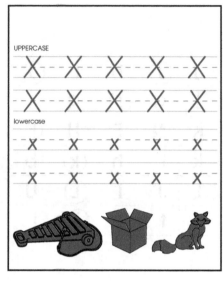

124

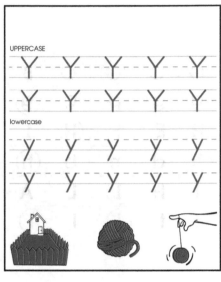

125

126

A	N	A	V	A
a	b	a	c	a
B	B	C	B	A
b	d	a	b	a
C	O	C	D	C
c	a	c	c	o

127

D	B	G	D	B
d	b	d	a	d
E	H	F	E	E
e	e	a	b	e
F	E	F	E	A
f	t	f	l	o

128

129

G	C	(G)	(O)	B
g	(g)	p	q	(g)
H	E	F	(H)	I
h	d	n	b	(h)
I	H	(I)	L	A
i	t	(i)	l	(i)

129

130

J	(J)	U	L	(J)
j	g	(j)	q	i
K	N	F	H	(K)
k	l	h	(k)	b
L	J	I	(L)	U
l	t	i	(l)	i

130

131

M	H	(M)	n	L
m	M	(a)	(m)	n
N	M	(N)	m	(N)
n	(n)	m	a	(n)
O	(O)	D	B	(O)
o	a	O	c	(O)

131

132

P	D	(P)	O	b
p	(p)	d	q	b
Q	O	(Q)	G	(Q)
q	p	(q)	d	b
R	(R)	B	P	(R)
r	(r)	n	m	(r)

132

133

S	P	(S)	B	(S)
s	o	a	(s)	e
T	I	P	L	(T)
t	f	l	(t)	i
U	(U)	D	(U)	O
u	(u)	n	m	n

133

134

V	W	(V)	A	N
v	w	x	(v)	y
W	V	M	A	(W)
w	(w)	v	x	m
X	Y	(X)	V	K
x	y	k	(x)	z

134

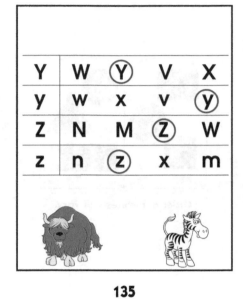

Y	W	(Y)	V	X
y	w	x	v	(y)
Z	N	M	(Z)	W
z	n	(z)	x	m

135

136

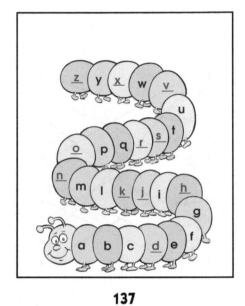

137

138

139

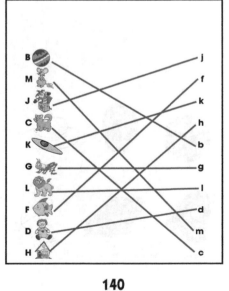

140

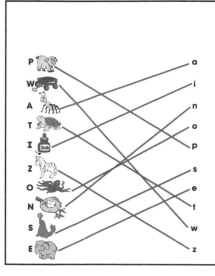

141

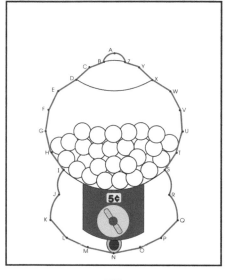

142

Order of pictures will vary.

143

How many things did Buddy put in his basket? 4

145

146

147

148

149

150

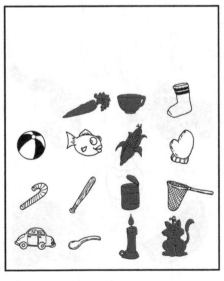

151

152

153

Mouse Magic

Help Michael Mouse perform magic.

154

Amazing Maze

Maggie wants to get to her mouse.

155

Dixie's Drawings

Dixie drew pictures of things that begin with **Dd**. Look at the pictures below.

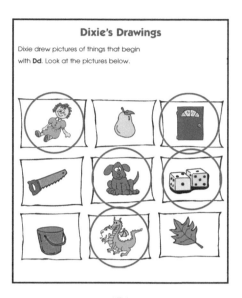

156

Order of pictures will vary.

157

Dd Mm Cc Ss

Cc Bb Tt Dd

Mm Tt Ss Bb

159

160

Waldo's Wall

Waldo is building a wall. Look at the pictures on it.

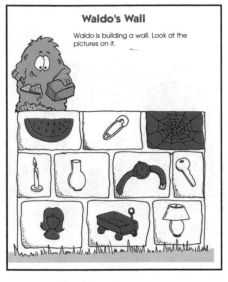

161

Jump, Jake, Jump!

Help Jake jump along the path.

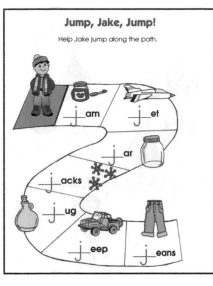

162

Jumping Jacks

163

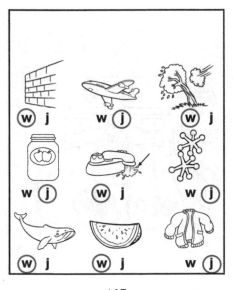

165

166

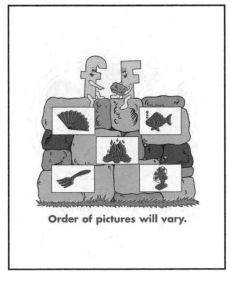

Order of pictures will vary.

167

169

Order of pictures
will vary.

171

172

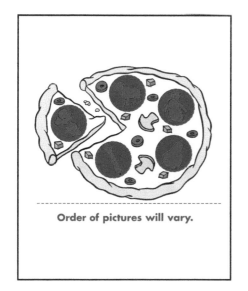

Order of pictures will vary.

173

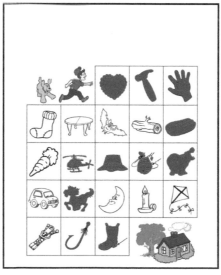

175

176

Order of pictures will vary.

177

179

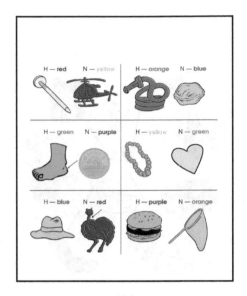

H — red	N — yellow	H — orange	N — blue
H — green	N — purple	H — yellow	N — green
H — blue	N — red	H — purple	N — orange

180

181

182

183

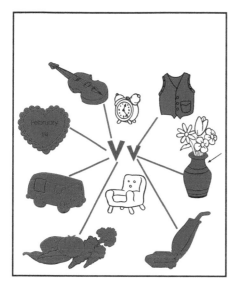

184

185

186

How many leaves are yellow? __4__
How many leaves are orange? __3__

187

188

189

190

Order of pictures will vary.

191

193

194

195

196

197

198

199

200

201

202

203

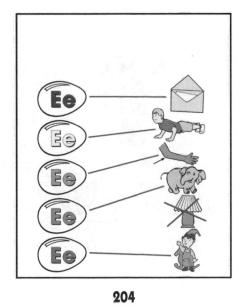

204

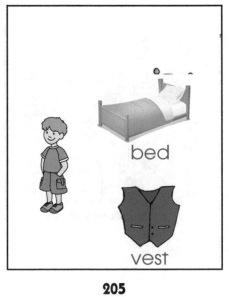

205

pen

desk

206

b_e_ll

t_e_nt

d_e_sk

h_e_n

n_e_st

v_e_st

dr_e_ss

207

a

a

e

e

e

a

a

a

e

e

208

Order of pictures will vary.

209

dish   mitt

211

212

213

214

215

216

217

218

bug   cub

219

duck   pup

220

221

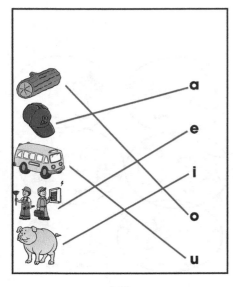

222

223

224

225

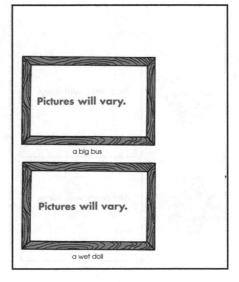

226

Pictures will vary.

six bugs

Pictures will vary.

ten rocks

227

map nest

dog frog

hat bat

kite mop

can fan

rat pig

233

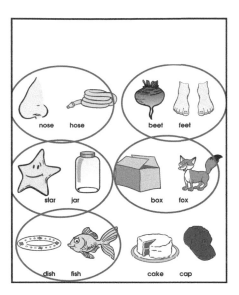

nose hose

beet feet

star jar

box fox

dish fish

cake cap

234

Answers will vary.

Answers will vary.

235

Answers will vary.

Answers will vary.

236

237/239

237/239

237/239

241

242

orange block   **pink** pig

purple balloon   **brown** bear

243

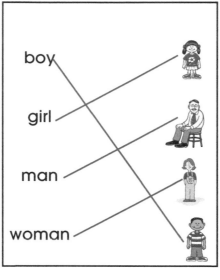

boy

girl

man

woman

244

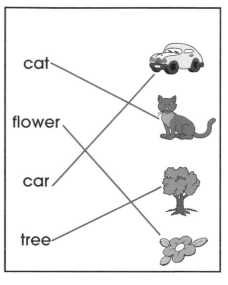

cat

flower

car

tree

245

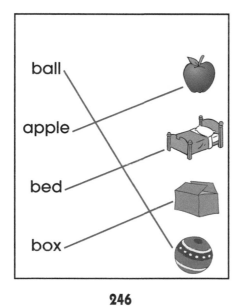

ball

apple

bed

box

246

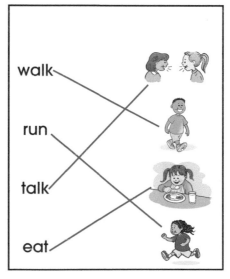

walk

run

talk

eat

247

248

play — (sand play)
ride — (sit/blocks)
sit — (bicycle)
cook — (girl cooking)

249

tall — (short ladder)
short — (elephant)
old — (old man)
big — (tall ladder)

250

little — (mouse)
happy — (clown)
sad — (crying face)
funny — (happy face)

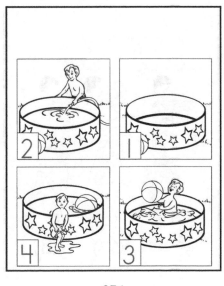

251

252

253

254

255

256

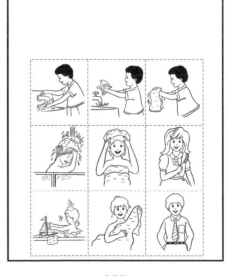

257

Answer Key

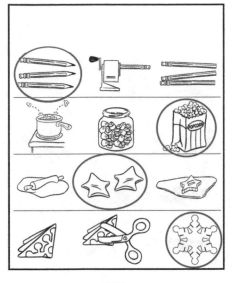

259

The first kitten wears silver bracelets and purple boots. It is pushing on the ball of green yarn.

The second kitten wears a red top hat. It is pulling on the ball of green yarn.

The third kitten is lounging on top of the ball of green yarn. It is wearing a blue T-shirt.

260

261

262

263

264

265

266

267

Grandma likes flowers that are pink.
She likes flowers that are tall.
She likes flowers that come with candy.

268

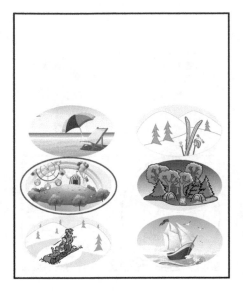

269

Zelda is playing basketball with her friends by the beach.

270

Miles and Melvin are brothers who love sleeping outside during the summer. One day, they both lie down on a big hammock.

271

Orville and his mother play guitar together.

272

273

274

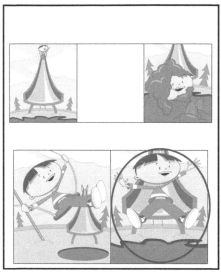

275

276

277

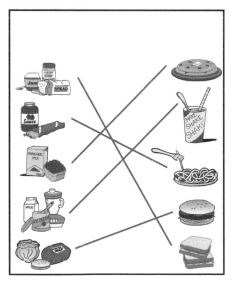

278

346

Answer Key

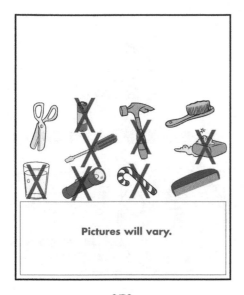

Pictures will vary.

279

Pictures will vary.

280

Pictures will vary.

281

Pictures will vary.

282

283

284

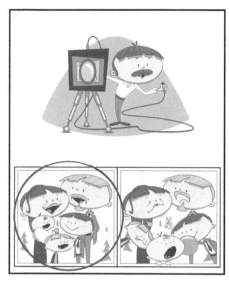

285

286

287

288

What words from the story begin with the same sound as 🐷 ?

fun (pizza) (pears) new

Circle the picture that rhymes with **Joy**.

Which word means the same as **small**?

new   funny   (little)

What did the child in this story think about school?

It was funny.   (It was fun.)

Who are Joy and Alan?

bears   (classmates)

289

What words from the story have the sound of **i** that you hear in **ride**?

run (bikes) (drive)

Circle the picture that rhymes with **school**.

Which word is the opposite of **early**?

nearby (late) many

Why do some children run to school?

They are early.   (They are late.)

How do you get to school? (Answers will vary.)

bus   car   walk   bike

290

What words from the story have the same sound as 🛷 ?

(we) early (walk) work

Circle the picture that rhymes with **walk**.

Which words in the story mean **Mom, Dad, and I together**?

(we) I (us) mom

Why does everyone get up early?

for lunch   (for breakfast)

Why doesn't Zip go to school?

Zip is a teacher.   (Zip is a cat.)

291

What words from the story begins with the blend you hear in ⏰ .

(class) plant counts

Circle the picture that rhymes with **plant**.

Which word in the story means **more than one book**?

paper   busy   (books)

What do the children do after they say "Good morning"?

They eat lunch. | They do their jobs. |

How do you like to help at school?

Kids will answer orally only.

292

What words from the story begins with the same sound as 🐑 sheep?

school   starts   (shoes)

What word in the story is made of two rhyming words?

school shoes   (backpack)

What word in the story is the name of a month?

indoors   Korea   (March)

Why do you think the children put on clean shoes in school?

Their feet hurt.   (Clean shoes keep the floors clean.)

How do children in your school carry their books?

backpack cloth bag lunch bag
(Answers will vary.)

293

What words in the story have the sound of **ou** that you hear in **pound**?

(our) lost (found) grown [playground] [how]

Circle the picture that rhymes with **fed**.

What word in the story is another word for **rabbit**?

baby   bumper   (bunny)

Who is Mr. Bell?

He is a rabbit.   (He is a teacher.)

Who is Bumper?

(She is a rabbit.) She is a teacher.

294

What word from the story rhymes with 🥄 ?

Petra   school   (cone)

Circle the picture that begins with the blend you hear at the beginning of **sweet**.

What word from the story is the opposite of **last**?

inside   (first)   pretty

What will make the first day sweet for Petra?

paper   (sweet things to eat)

Name some things that could be in Petra's cone.

shoes   paper   (candy)

295

Find two words in the story that rhyme with **stick**.

first (kick) liked (Nick)

Circle the picture that begins with the same sound you hear at the beginning of **home**.

Which word in the story is the opposite of **outside**?

new   home   (inside)

Why did Evan feel alone?

He was hungry.   (It was his first day.)

What did Nick do to help Evan?

(Nick asked Evan to play ball.
Nick sat beside Evan. Nick said, "See you!")

296

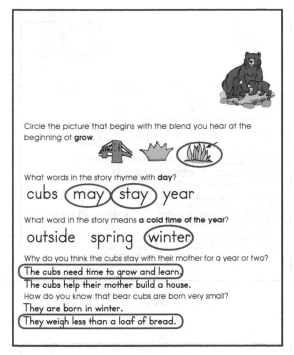

Circle the picture that begins with the blend you hear at the beginning of **grow**.

What words in the story rhyme with **day**?

cubs (may) (stay) year

What word in the story means **a cold time of the year**?

outside   spring   (winter)

Why do you think the cubs stay with their mother for a year or two?

(The cubs need time to grow and learn.)
The cubs help their mother build a house.
How do you know that bear cubs are born very small?
They are born in winter.
(They weigh less than a loaf of bread.)

297

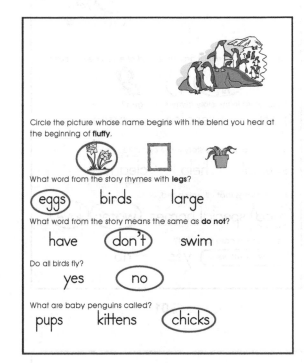

Circle the picture whose name begins with the blend you hear at the beginning of **fluffy**.

What word from the story rhymes with **legs**?

(eggs)   birds   large

What word from the story means the same as **do not**?

have   (don't)   swim

Do all birds fly?

yes   (no)

What are baby penguins called?

pups   kittens   (chicks)

298

What word in the story begins like 🪑 ?

some   (change)   rest

What word in the story rhymes with **hear**?

home   (deer)   from

What word in the story is the opposite of **go**?

one   move   (stop)

Where is a deer's home?
(where it stops to rest for the day)
where it walks

Why do you think some animals move from place to place?

(to look for food)   to find a soft pillow

299

Circle the picture that has the sound of **e** you hear in **pet**.

Circle the picture that names a word that rhymes with **goat**.

Which word in the story is a day of the week?

last   (Saturday)   show

Where does the bike path go?

(to the fair)   to the pet shop

Why will Grandma need a new hat?
A goat wore her hat.   (A goat ate her hat.)

300

Circle the picture that has the sound of **e** you hear in **need**.

What word in the story rhymes with **gets**?
(pets)　exercise　care

What word from the story is the opposite of **dirty**?
special　help　(clean)

Name things that all pets need.
(food)　special homes　(water)(love)

Do you help care for a pet?
(Answers will vary.)　yes　no

301

Circle the picture that has the sound of **oo** you hear in **food**.

What words from the story rhyme with **blue**?
used　(grew)　good　(you)

What word from the story means **more than one dinosaur**?
(dinosaurs)　eggs　plants

What does **Maiasaura** mean?
(good mother lizard)　soft and warm

How was this dinosaur a good mother?
(She made a soft nest.　She brought food.)
She sang songs.

302

What word from the story begins like **smile**?
wings　(smooth)　bat

What word from the story rhymes with **sings**?
size　thin　(wings)

What word from the story means **having fur**?
bird　smooth　(furry)

How is a bat different from all other mammals?
It is furry.　(It can fly.)

What is different about a bat's bones?
They are smooth.　(They are light.)

303

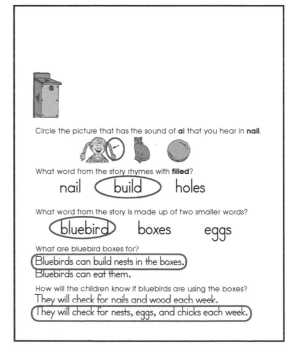

Circle the picture that has the sound of **ai** that you hear in **nail**.

What word from the story rhymes with **filled**?
nail　(build)　holes

What word from the story is made up of two smaller words?
(bluebird)　boxes　eggs

What are bluebird boxes for?
(Bluebirds can build nests in the boxes.)
Bluebirds can eat them.

How will the children know if bluebirds are using the boxes?
They will check for nails and wood each week.
(They will check for nests, eggs, and chicks each week.)

304